D1366785

HYDROSTATIC EXTRUSION

Other titles in this series

TL/ME/2 THE HEAT PIPE
D Chisholm

Other Mechanical Engineering titles available

ME/1 TRIBOLOGY
E D Hondros

ME/2 ELECTRON BEAM WELDING
M J Fletcher

ME/3 VACUUM BRAZING
M J Fletcher

ME/4 STRESS CORROSION FAILURE
P Greenfield

ME/5 GLOW DISCHARGE MATERIAL PROCESSING
R A Dugdale

All published by Mills & Boon Limited.

M & B Technical Library TL/ME/1

General Editor: J Gordon Cook, PhD, FRIC

Hydrostatic Extrusion

J M Alexander
DSc(Eng), PhD, FCGI, DIC
FIMechE, FIProdE, FIM, FRSA

Professor of Applied Mechanics
Imperial College of Science and Technology, University of London

B Lengyel
PhD, DIC, Dipl Ing, FIMechE

Lecturer in Mechanical Engineering
Imperial College of Science and Technology, University of London

Mills & Boon Limited
London

First published in Great Britain 1971
by Mills & Boon Limited, 17–19 Foley Street,
London W1A 1DR

ISBN 0 263 51709 8

Made and printed in Great Britain by
Butler & Tanner Limited, Frome and London

TS
255
.A34

CONTENTS

PREFACE

The process of hydrostatic extrusion has many advantages in its favour, primarily associated with the almost complete elimination of friction between the billet and its container and the consequent possibility of extruding very long billets of dimensions which do not have to be closely controlled. This, in its turn, leads to the possibility of the semi-continuous or continuous extrusion of long prismatic lengths of feed stock, hitherto impossible. When this is coupled with the use of hydrostatic pressure to enable isostatic compaction of powders, the process becomes extremely attractive.

The design of equipment to achieve hydrostatic extrusion and isostatic compaction on a viable production basis introduces many problems, in relation to both the containment of high pressure and effective sealing and clamping in the dynamic situations involved in repeated extrusion and semi continuous and continuous operation. The choice of fluids and the possibility of operating at temperatures somewhat above ambient also introduce problems.

For these reasons the authors, who have both spent several years undertaking research into these processes at Imperial College under the sponsorship of the Science Research Council, thought that it might be useful to give an account of their findings together with a broad description of the developments made by other workers in the field, notably those in the U.S.A. at Harvard and the Battelle Memorial Institute, in Russia at the High Pressure Laboratory in Moscow, in the U.K. at the National Engineering Laboratory, in Sweden at the firm of A.S.E.A., and in other laboratories throughout the world. More and more researchers have become interested in the process and made significant developments which will undoubtedly lead to its eventual adoption by industry. It is therefore difficult to give due acknowledgement to all those who have contributed to our understanding of this process and to pick out really significant developments from the industrial point of view. Also, despite strenuous efforts, it has often been difficult to find the earliest reference out of a large number of publications, so slight discrepancies in this respect may have occurred. Sincere apologies are due in such cases: these are entirely unintentional and imply neither depreciation nor disregard for the particular research and development effort.

Generally SI units have been used in the monograph, but in some cases other units are shown, in illustrations or tables reproduced from references.

Permission to make use of illustrations from published works is gratefully acknowledged. It would be difficult to mention individually each colleague and publisher at this stage, who gave permission so kindly and willingly: all such information is given in the footnotes and in the reference list.

We are indebted to Mr Peter Ashford who helped in the reading of the proofs and the preparation of the illustrations.

J. M. ALEXANDER
B. LENGYEL
Imperial College 1971

1. Introduction

Hydrostatic extrusion is a method of extruding metals by surrounding a billet with a fluid and raising the pressure of the fluid to a point at which the billet is forced through the aperture or apertures in the die (Fig. 1). Many problems must be overcome in order to achieve hydrostatic extrusion even on a laboratory scale; these are connected mainly with sealing the high pressure fluid, and controlling the rate of extrusion and the lubrication conditions. As most fluids cannot be used satisfactorily at very high temperatures, hydrostatic extrusion is generally

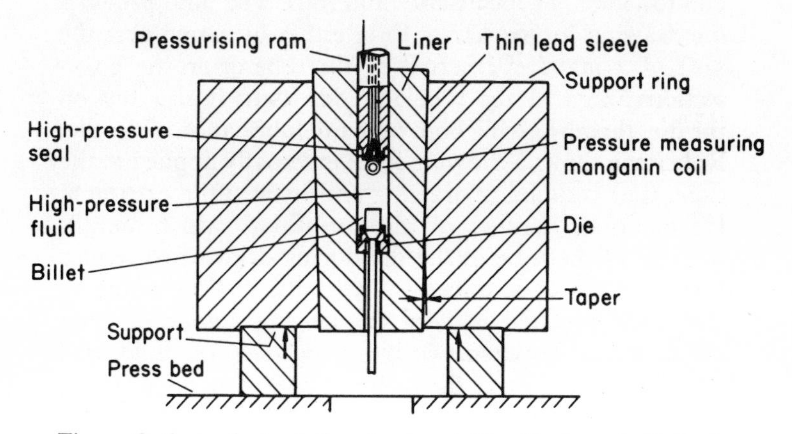

Fig. 1. Orthodox hydrostatic extrusion. (*After Pugh* et al, *Ref. 9.*)

carried out at room temperature; extremely high fluid pressures may be required, therefore, possibly as high as 30 kbar. This introduces difficulties in the design of containers strong enough to withstand repeated pressurisation at these high levels, and in developing seals for the rams or plungers used to generate the pressure. These difficulties are accentuated when more complicated versions of the basic process of hydrostatic extrusion are considered, such as fluid-to-fluid extrusion, augmented hydrostatic extrusion, and semi-continuous hydrostatic extrusion. Nevertheless, the basic process and its variants have great potentialities both from the point of view of the quality of the product and the economics of the process, and considerable interest has been shown in attempting to develop commercially viable processes. This review describes the mechanics of the process and traces its main historical development; it considers the present state of the theoretical and experimental background in relation to the possible industrial development and application of hydrostatic extrusion.

The earliest process of hydrostatic extrusion seems to have been that patented by Robertson in 1893,[1] and mentioned by Johnson in his Introductory Address[2] and later by Kronberger.[3] This patent relates to the extrusion and drawing of tubes, plates and rods. The fluid provides the drawing (or extrusion) force either by acting over the area of a mandrel inserted in the tube or on the cross-sectional area of the tube (or rod) itself; it also acts on the die, thereby giving high pressure lubrication of the die. Robertson shows a drawing force externally applied to the tube, thus combining drawing and hydrostatic extrusion. He mentions another of his inventions, which entails rotation of the tube in the die during drawing to reduce friction. He also describes a "hydraulic die" for reducing the loads required in wire drawing by admitting high pressure fluid between two dies which seal the fluid, and mentions pressures of the order of 6400 bar for drawing iron and steel wire.

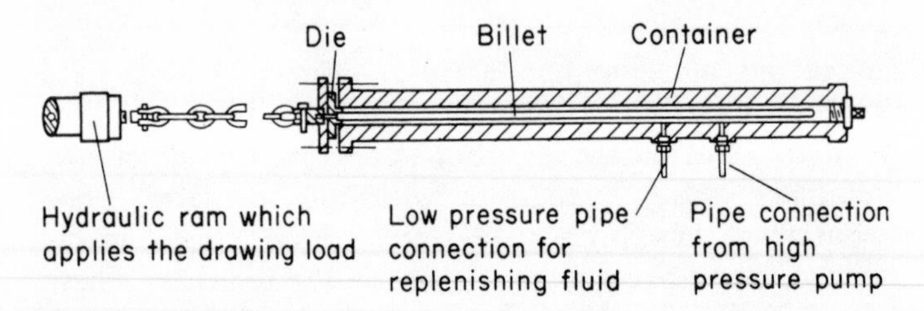

Fig. 2. Hydrostatic extrusion with product augmentation. (After J. Robertson, Ref. 1.)

Many of these ideas have been put forward quite

recently in connection with metal working processes by investigators who were clearly unaware of Robertson's inventions, and he was undoubtedly many years ahead of his time. Fig. 2 is a reproduction of Fig. 7 of his patent specification showing the combined hydrostatic extrusion and drawing of a rod, now known as hydrostatic extrusion with product augmentation.

The first scientific examination of hydrostatic extrusion was made by the late Professor Bridgman at Harvard University, U.S.A.[4] He did not carry out much experimental work on this subject and encountered some difficulties in his experiments; these were concerned mainly with the high-speed ejection of the metal at the highest pressures, and the heat developed as a result of high extrusion velocities. Bridgman also investigated the properties of extruded wires as compared with drawn wires, but the results were insufficient to be conclusive.

Following on from Bridgman's researches was the work by Pugh and his colleagues at the National Engineering Laboratory, U.K. Pugh has given a comprehensive summary of this work and of other researches in his Bulleid Memorial Lecture,[5] based on previous publications.[6–13] Pugh and his colleagues have investigated the process in great detail, paying particular attention to the determination of the extrusion pressure, and they have examined a great variety of important engineering materials. They have also considered the theoretical analysis of the problem and measured the properties of hydrostatically extruded products, particularly those extruded into a back pressure (by fluid-to-fluid extrusion).

Independently, and at about the same time, work commenced at the ultra-high pressure laboratory of the Academy of Sciences in Moscow by Beresnev, Vereshchagin, Ryabinin and their colleagues.[14–22] A summary of their early work appears in the book by Beresnev *et al.*[23] These researches confirmed that hydrostatic extrusion had many advantages over the conventional method of cold extrusion—for example, extrusion pressures were reduced (mainly by elimination of container-wall friction but also by reduction of friction in the die) and the optimum die angle was small, so that more uniform deformation occurred over the cross-section of the extrudate. It was found also that higher strength was imparted by hydrostatic extrusion than by conventional drawing methods, and this was attributed to the increased density of the metal by the closure of internal voids and pores under hydrostatic extrusion conditions. Investigation of behaviour in hydrostatic extrusion at high temperature was also made. In general, a linear relationship between hydrostatic extrusion pressure and $\ln R$ was found to exist (R = extrusion ratio); pressure dropped off markedly as the temperature was increased up to 300°C for aluminium extruded using a mixture of 75% kerosene and 25% transformer oil.

Many other research workers have taken an interest in hydrostatic extrusion, including Randall *et al.*[24] at Nuclear Metals Inc., Fiorentino *et al.*[25] at the Battelle Memorial Institute, Bobrowsky[26] of the Pressure Technology Corporation of America, Rozner and Faupel[27] of Du Pont in the U.S.A., Green[28] at the United Kingdom Atomic Authority (U.K.A.E.A.) and Alexander, Lengyel *et al.* at Imperial College.[29–32]

Interest in the process has increased over the years, and at a conference on High Pressure Engineering organised in September 1967 by the Institution of Mechanical Engineers, there were seven papers[33–39] on hydrostatic extrusion, and several others on closely related topics (e.g. Ref. 40). At the International Institution for Production Engineering Research (C.I.R.P.) Conference in Nottingham and the Machine Tool Design and Research (M.T.D.R.) Conference in Birmingham in September 1968 a number of papers related to hydrostatic extrusion.[41–49]

In addition to the papers mentioned in this introduction there are many more which will be referred to later in the appropriate context.

2. Mechanics of the Process

2.1 ORTHODOX HYDROSTATIC EXTRUSION

The basic method of hydrostatic extrusion, illustrated in Fig. 1, is called "free", "simple", or "orthodox" hydrostatic extrusion. The advantages of the process are as follows:

(i) Friction between billet and container is absent; long billets can be extruded without a corresponding increase in the extrusion pressure.

(ii) Since friction between die and billet is low, dies of small angle may be used to reduce redundant deformation and extrusion pressure. Harder materials can be cold extruded because shearing of the billet along the die face—which could lead to fracture in conventional extrusion—is reduced.

(iii) Within limits, it is not necessary to use cylindrical billets of closely controlled dimensions. Non-straight billets, or coils of wire with free or clamped back-end, can be extruded into straight products. The cladding of long lengths of wire is also possible.

(iv) Support can be given to the die by surrounding it with the high pressure fluid. Products of complex section can be extruded through thin-walled dies.

(v) The process is versatile. Simple die replacement enables billets of various sizes and sections to be extruded. Stepped products can be produced.

(vi) The strength of the extruded wire is more often higher than in conventional wire drawing owing to the absence of internal voids and pores in extrusion under large compressive stresses.

Possible disadvantages are as follows:

(i) Considerable compression of the fluid has to occur (typically up to one-third of the volume) to generate sufficiently high pressures (e.g. 30 kbar). This results in large amounts of stored energy, which reduces efficiency and may be dangerous.

(ii) The billet must be tapered at its front end and held against the die to effect initial sealing.

(iii) Once the billet has begun to extrude it is difficult to control the rate of extrusion. Consequently, extrusion speed is often too high; undesirable heating and softening of the billet may occur. In such cases the billet and fluid are ejected violently from the container unless some means of control is provided. Lack of control of the extrusion speed often leads to instability, which is characterised by "stick-slip" movement of the extrudate and fluctuating pressure-time characteristics.

(iv) In production, containment of fluid requires ancillary equipment if a horizontal arrangement is used. A large number of repeated cycles of operation may necessitate frequent changes of the seal between the moving punch and static container, or the development of special sealing arrangements. This may cause fatigue of containers, punches and other items.

It is difficult to overcome many of these disadvantages inherent in the basic process. Both Crawley *et al.*[33] and Low *et al.*[34] describe a cap which can be sealed on to the trailing end of the billet and is a close fit in the container, as illustrated in Fig. 3. Since there is only a small annular orifice around the cap, any sudden forward movement of the billet will cause the pressure behind the cap to diminish due to the restriction on fluid flow through the orifice, thus damping out the oscillation due to the "stick-slip" behaviour mentioned above. In the case of simple product shapes, such as round rod, it is possible to attach a hard conical plug to the trailing end of the billet (Fig. 4); at the end of extrusion, the die is sealed by the hard plug and violent decompression and ejection of the fluid are thereby prevented. It would be possible to combine this plug with the cap previously described.

The hydrostatic extrusion of hollow sections is achievable only by using a mandrel of either a stationary or moving type; a typical arrangement for the former is as shown in Fig. 5. Provision must be made for an initial

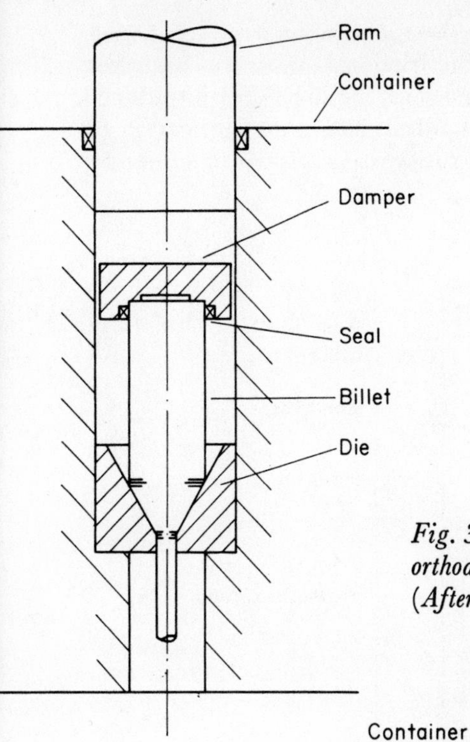

Fig. 3. Damping arrangement for orthodox hydrostatic extrusion. (*After Low* et al., *Ref. 34.*)

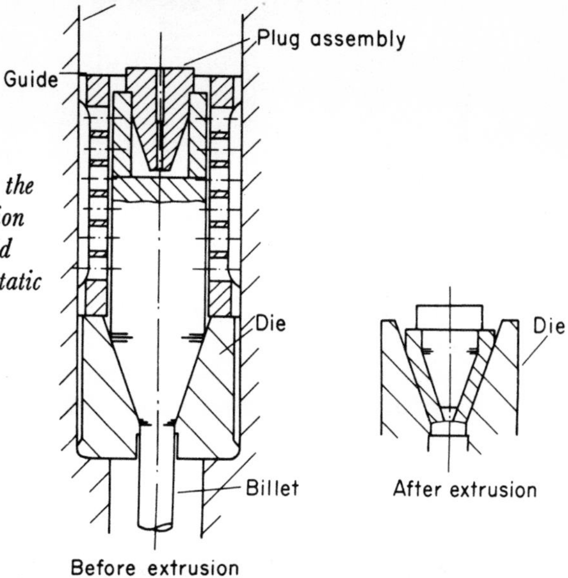

Fig. 4. Preventing the violent decompression and ejection of fluid in orthodox hydrostatic extrusion.

seal to be made between the mandrel and the top of the tube. There is considerable friction between the mandrel and the tube in the vicinity of the die. This introduces tensile stresses into the mandrel, and good lubrication of the mandrel prior to extrusion is necessary to minimise its effect.

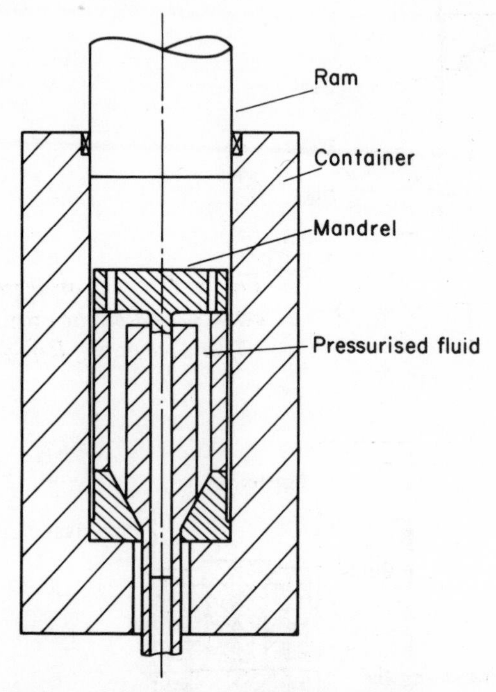

Fig. 5. Hydrostatic extrusion of hollow sections.

If the hardness of a moving mandrel were similar to that of the tubular billet, then both would be reduced during hydrostatic extrusion; this raises the possibility of the extrusion of composite billets or clad products. Metals such as aluminium and copper, copper and brass or silver, and different alloy steels could be co-extruded in this way.

The forming of stepped products is another possible application of hydrostatic extrusion. Each end of the extrusion can be hydrostatically extruded separately, because the shape of the billet within the extrusion container is immaterial, as illustrated in Fig. 6. As it is necessary to open the container, change the die and/or reverse the product before each extrusion, it may be more economical to forge or machine the product from the solid, but the process may have attractions for the manufacture of components of non-circular cross-section.

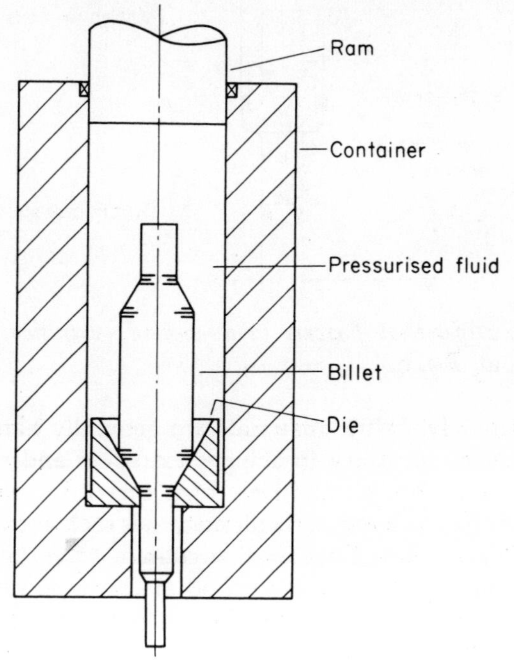

Fig. 6. Hydrostatic extrusion of stepped products. (After Pugh, Ref. 5.)

2.2 FLUID-TO-FLUID EXTRUSION

In "fluid-to-fluid" or "differential pressure" extrusion the extrudate is surrounded by fluid at a lower pressure than the fluid surrounding the billet. A diagrammatic arrangement of apparatus used for this process is shown in Fig. 7. The effective pressure causing extrusion is the difference between the pressures of the two fluids. The main advantage of the process lies in the suppression of fracture of more brittle materials by the superimposed back pressure.

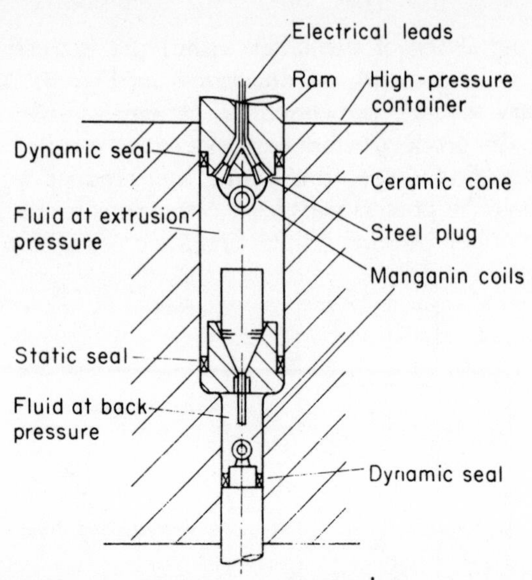

Fig. 7. Differential pressure (fluid-to-fluid) extrusion. (After Pugh et al, *Ref. 9.)*

Unfortunately, brittle materials are generally hard, and the pressure necessary to achieve extrusion and prevent fracture are often prohibitively high except for small reductions. Nevertheless, difficult materials such as cast iron, molybdenum, beryllium and zirconium have been extruded successfully by this method at extrusion ratios up to 3 : 1, and an aluminium-silicon alloy ("silumin") has been extruded at a ratio of 6 : 1.[5]

Most of the advantages and disadvantages of the basic hydrostatic extrusion process already listed apply to fluid-to-fluid extrusion. An additional difficulty is the need to control the two fluid pressures. As the extrudate enters the lower chamber the pressure will rise unless some means of retracting the plunger is provided. A typical method is to provide a constant pressure relief valve in the hydraulic system actuating the lower plunger.

2.3 AUGMENTED HYDROSTATIC EXTRUSION

The enormous pressures required in hydrostatic extrusion

may be reduced, and the extrusion speed controlled, by additionally pushing or pulling the billet into the die; these techniques, often called billet and product augmentation, respectively, were suggested originally by Robertson[1]. The first method, adopted in the U.K.A.E.A. under the name "augmented hydrostatic extrusion", is described by Slater and Green.[37] The process is shown in Fig. 8, the principle of operation being that a plunger is sealed at each end into two containers, the upper container being of larger diameter than the lower. There is a hole along the axis of the plunger interconnecting the two containers, so that the same fluid pressure exists in each. Due to the larger diameter of the top container there is an out-of-

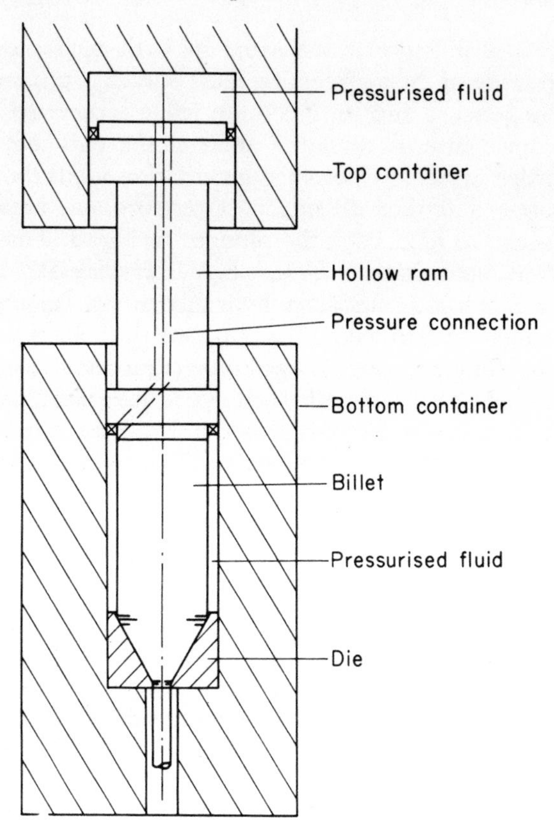

Fig. 8. Augmented hydrostatic extrusion. Billet augmentation (After Slater et al., *Ref. 37.)*

balance force which is applied to the billet, augmenting the hydrostatic extrusion pressure. As the billet is extruded from the lower container, some interchange of fluid takes place until at the end of extrusion virtually all the fluid has been exhausted from the lower container. This is advantageous in that it minimises the large energy release which takes place at the end of orthodox hydrostatic extrusion. Also, it is possible to establish greater control over the extrusion rate, since the relative motion of the billet and the die can be controlled by controlling the ram speed. The troublesome "stick-slip" phenomenon commonly encountered in conventional hydrostatic extrusion is damped down or eliminated completely.

Since the pressure is the same in both containers, the magnitude of the augmenting load is always proportional to the pressure and its maximum value is dictated by the difference in cross-sectional areas of the two containers. In order to achieve lower augmentation loads for billets of softer materials or smaller cross-sectional area, it is necessary to hold back the plunger in Fig. 8. This is the method used in the U.K.A.E.A. "Hydrostat" and it necessitates using ancillary hydraulic rams. Another disadvantage of this method is that two containers and one hollow plunger (which may also be regarded as a pressure vessel) are used, all with high cyclic internal fluid pressure. In comparison with orthodox hydrostatic extrusion, the number of pressure vessels subjected to large stress cycles and fatigue is thus increased from one to three.

Perhaps the simplest method of achieving billet augmentation is that described by the authors[36] as applied to the semi-continuous hydrostatic extrusion process. Its application to the extrusion of straight billets is illustrated in Fig. 9. The concentric annular plungers and the die may be at the same or at opposite ends of the extrusion container, as shown in Fig. 9(*a*) and (*b*). In this way the pressurising and direct loading of the billet may be separated and controlled independently. This method is called "compound extrusion" to distinguish it from augmented extrusion previously described. It has the advantage that, by dividing the area of the container into two parts, it reduces the operating forces needed for each of the dual plungers. As there is no ancillary ram, the required ram force is reduced in all but the few cases when the full available direct load is used in augmented extrusion. Furthermore, since only one container is subjected to high cyclic internal pressures, the possibility of fatigue failure is minimised. Finally, the fluid volume that must be compressed in compound extrusion is smaller for identical billets; this represents a decrease in the stored fluid energy, which is an important safety consideration. It will also reduce the work that must be expended to compress the fluid.

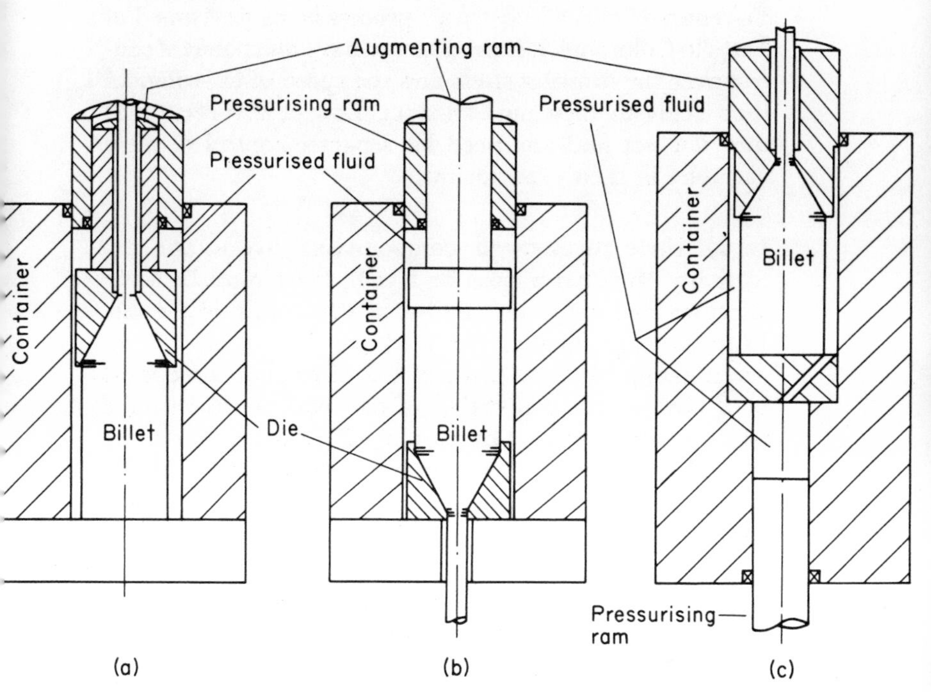

Fig. 9. Compound extrusion. Billet augmentation. (*After Lengyel* et al., *Ref. 36.*)

Another method of compound extrusion is illustrated in Fig. 9(*c*). The top plunger contains the die and provides augmentation, whilst the bottom plunger provides pressurisation. In all three alternatives, the pressurising plunger must be allowed to move during extrusion in order to maintain the fluid pressure at a constant level.

The hydrostatic extrusion pressure can be reduced also by the addition of a tensile pull on the extrudate, as originally described by Robertson in his patent[1] and later suggested by Bridgman[4] and Low *et al.*[34] It seems likely that the augmentation of the extrusion force by the tensile pull can be kept completely separate from the pressurising force supplied by the hydrostatic extrusion plunger. Practical realisation of this concept appears to present difficulties; according to the discussion by Sabroff and Fiorentino[51] of the "Hydraw" process being developed at Battelle-Columbus, it is necessary to have independent control over the drawing stress and the speed of drawing. In their reply to these investigators, Low *et al.*[34] state that they did not find any need for separate control of these variables in their experiments.

In all these methods of compounding hydrostatic extrusion with either a push or a pull, there must be some effect on the lubrication conditions which exist in the die. With the exception of the work by Parsons *et al.*[45] no investigation has been made of this effect, but there must be a limit to the proportion of the total extrusion force which can be provided by pushing or pulling the material through the die if the good lubrication conditions induced there by the hydrostatic pressure are to be maintained.

2.4 SEMI-CONTINUOUS AND CONTINUOUS HYDROSTATIC EXTRUSION; HYDROSPIN

In all the described cases of billet augmentation there is clearly a limitation on the length of billet which can be extruded. Consideration must be given to the possibility of buckling of the billet and/or of the plungers if they are too long, and these are the main reasons for developing the semi-continuous process.

In semi-continuous hydrostatic extrusion, which the authors suggested first and patented in 1965,[53] unlimited lengths of feed stock in the form of round or rectangular cross-section bar can be hydrostatically extruded by introducing it into the container through a clamping device, as shown in Fig. 10. On pressurising the fluid, the billet material is bent in the container until the fluid reaches the required extrusion pressure, whereupon hydrostatic extrusion begins and the feed stock extrudes out until it becomes almost straight. Pressure is then released by withdrawing the plunger, the clamping jaws release the billet and a further length of billet may be introduced into the container and the process repeated.

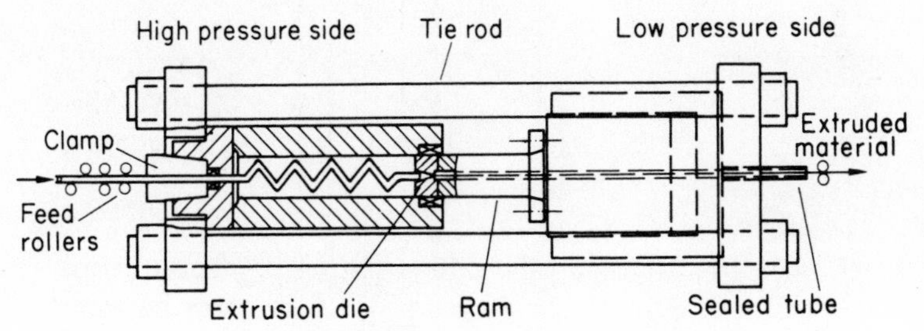

Fig. 10. Semi-continuous hydrostatic extrusion of flexible billets. (*After Alexander* et al., *Ref. 29.*)

The process described above suffers from the disadvantage that it is necessary to bend the feed stock; also, on initially withdrawing the plunger to depressurise the fluid, the seal may be broken between die and extrudate with consequent loss of fluid. To overcome these disadvantages the dual-plunger arrangement shown in Fig. 11 was devised, which allows separate pressurisation of the fluid and movement of the die in relation to the billet material. This enables close control of the extrusion speed to be established, eliminates the necessity for bending the feed stock, and allows compound extrusion to be effected. In the U.K.A.E.A. version of this process, clamping is achieved by a cylindrical tapered steel sleeve with axial slots, surrounded by a rubber sleeve for sealing against the fluid. Several other versions have been developed, e.g.

by N.E.L. and Vickers, but the main features are the same as those already described.

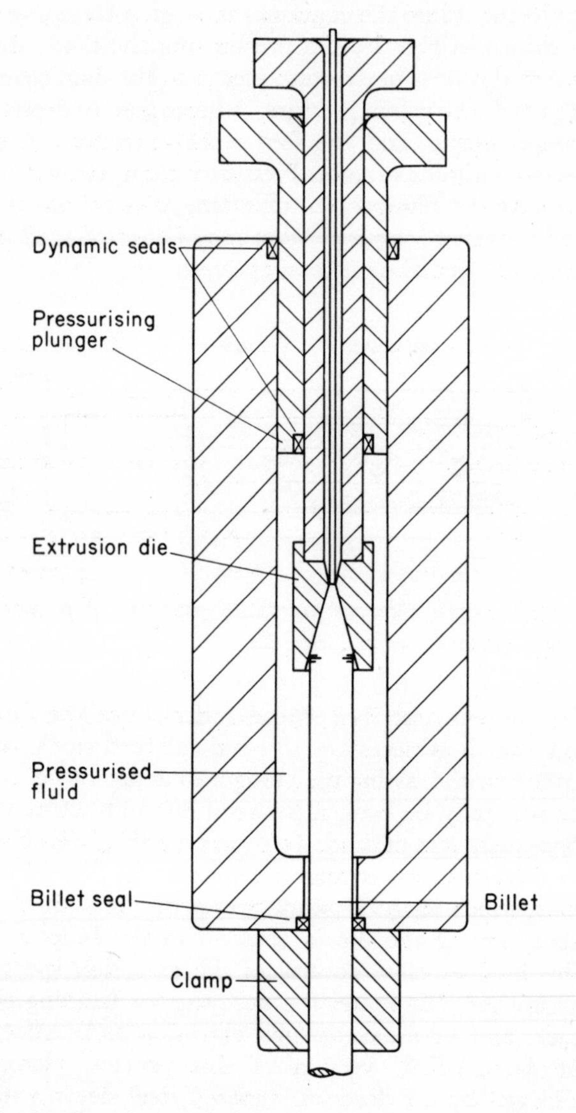

Fig. 11. Semi-continuous hydrostatic extrusion using the compounding principle.

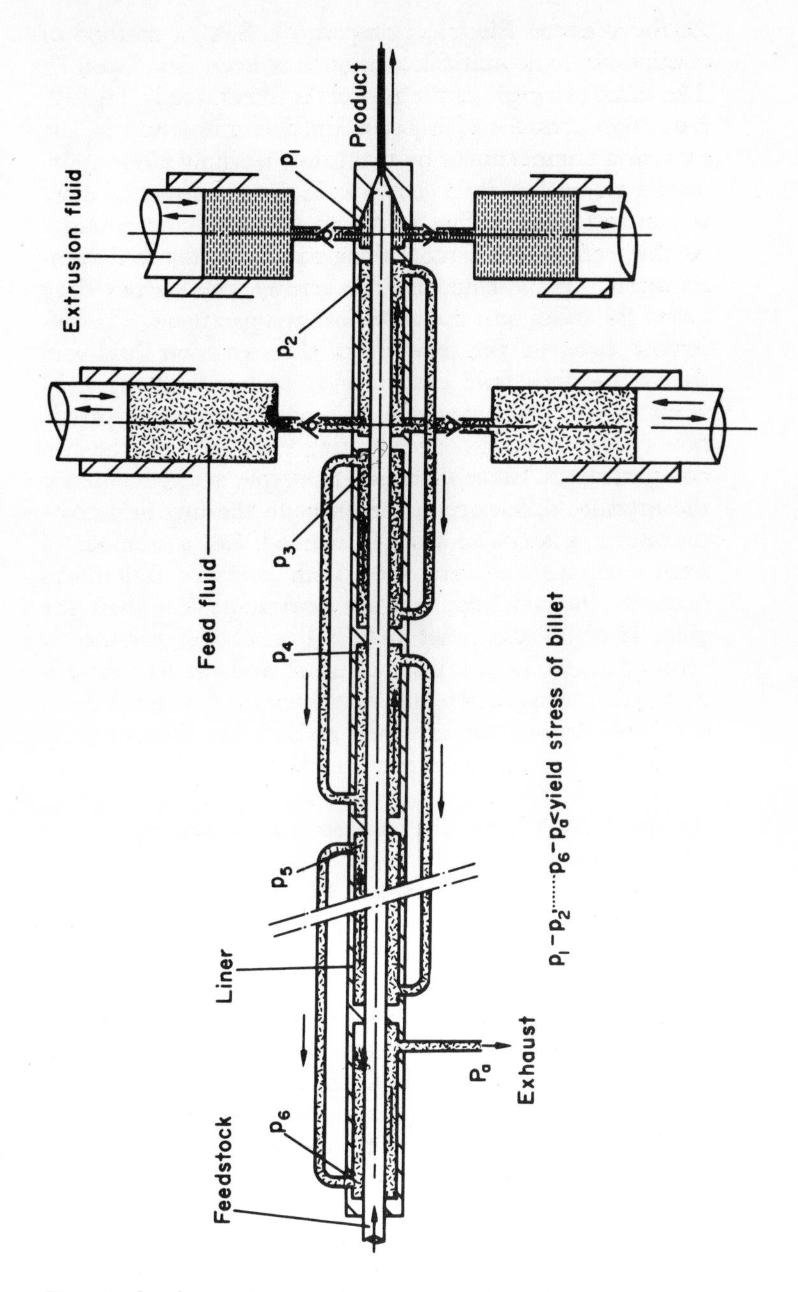

Fig. 12. Continuous hydrostatic extrusion. (*After Fuchs, Ref. 134.*)

At the Western Electric Company, U.S.A., a method of continuous hydrostatic extrusion has been developed.[134] The basic principle of the process is illustrated in Fig. 12. Extrusion pressure p_1 is maintained continuously in the extrusion compartment by two rams, working alternately. Similarly, the feed fluid (beeswax in the experimental unit) is pumped into the first feed compartment continuously. As the feed fluid is forced along axially in the feed compartment (as indicated by the arrow), the viscous drag forces the billet into the extrusion compartment. The difference between the pressure of the extrusion fluid and that of the feed fluid clearly must be less than the yield stress of the billet material, in order to prevent plastic flow of the billet at the separating wall between the two compartments. Since the same principle is applicable for the pressure difference at the entry to the first feed compartment, a series of steps is needed, i.e. a number of feed compartments are used with pressure differences between the neighbouring compartments less than the yield stress of the billet material, until the pressure is reduced to the atmospheric pressure and the feed fluid is dumped to exhaust. Heated liners are used in the bore of the feed compartments; they reduce the viscous drag along the walls and improve the efficiency of the process.

At the U.K.A.E.A., the process called Hydrospin has been developed; this is a combination of hydrostatic extrusion, conventional extrusion, turning and another conventional extrusion.[135] An exploded view of the tooling is shown in Fig. 13.

In the first stage, the billet of initial cross sectional area A_0 is hydrostatically extruded through a conical die which is splined to resist rotation of the billet and, simultaneously, over a piercing cone by conventional extrusion. The billet is thus reduced to a tube of cross sectional area A_1. A rotating tool then removes "swarf" of cross sectional area A_2 which is immediately forced through a conventional extrusion die to emerge as a product of cross-sectional area A_3. A feature of the process is that the billet material is entirely confined within the tools, with the exception of area A_3. Clearly, the final reduction A_0/A_3 is the product of the reductions in the various stages and, if the area A_2 is small, very small diameter wire could be produced from large diameter billets by the application of relatively small forces. In fact, the main role of hydrostatic extrusion in this case is to feed the billet material to the rotating tool, thus the reduction (and the fluid pressure) could be kept relatively small at this stage.

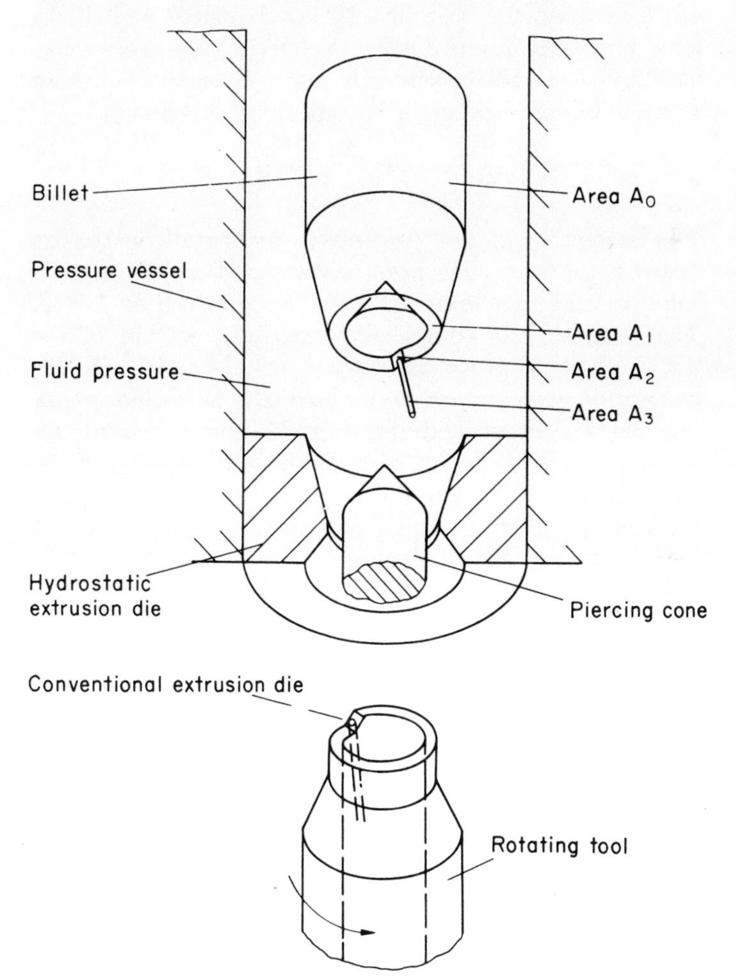

Fig. 13. Exploded view of Hydrospin tooling. (After Green, Ref. 135.)

2.5 HYDROSTATIC EXTRUSION BY EXPLOSIVES

The possibility of hydrostatic extrusion using explosive energy has been investigated by Johnson and Travis.[38,39] Black powder confined in oil was ignited electrically and billets of aluminium extruded through dies of 20°, 40° and 60° included angle. Typically extruded billets were of $1\frac{1}{2}$ in diameter, initially $2\frac{3}{4}$ in. diameter and 12 in long, requiring about 2 lbf of explosive. Most success was obtained when billets were only partly extruded, but there seems to be some difficulty in controlling this process.

2.6 HOT HYDROSTATIC EXTRUSION

The possibility of hot (or warm) hydrostatic extrusion appears to have first been investigated by Beresnev[17] using a container designed for 10kb pressure at 400°C. The product was completely extruded, ejection of the hot fluid being prevented by a "cut-off cone". The investigation was confined to commercially pure aluminium, and Beresnev examined various fluid-lubricant combinations. For this particular material, at temperatures in the range 20–340°C, he found that a mixture of graphite and lubricating grease in equal proportions gave the lowest hydrostatic extrusion pressures.

More recently, Sauve[54] has used mixtures of paraffin wax, heavy oil, graphite and molybdenum disulphide placed in the container of a conventional extrusion press in such a way as effectively to promote hydrostatic extrusion of the billet. He achieved very high temperatures in this way (up to 1100°C).

3. Theoretical Background

3.1 GENERAL DISCUSSION

In any metal working process the work required can be split into three components:

(i) useful work
(ii) redundant work
(iii) friction work

(i) *Useful work*
If there were no losses in the extrusion process the extrusion pressure p would be given by the expression:

$$p = \int_0^{\varepsilon_1} Y d\varepsilon \qquad (1)$$

which represents the work done per unit volume in the pure extension of the billet up to the strain

$$\varepsilon_1 = \ln R = \ln \frac{A_1}{A_2} \qquad (2)$$

In these equations Y is the yield stress at strain ε, R is the extrusion ratio, A_1 is the initial cross-sectional area, A_2 the final cross-sectional area. The integral in equation (1) is the area under the stress/strain curve for the conditions of the process, it being remembered that Y is actually a function of strain rate and temperature as well as strain. Under hydrostatic extrusion conditions both strain rate and hence temperature may be high, so that taking the "static" stress/strain curve may lead to error. For an approximate estimate of extrusion pressure it is often adequate to use a mean value of the yield or flow stress Y_m, in which case equation (1) can be integrated directly to give:

$$p = Y_m \ln R \qquad (3)$$

(ii) *Redundant work*
The flow conditions for a material being hydrostatically extruded through a conical die are far removed from those

of pure extension. Originally transverse plane cross-sections certainly do not remain plane; they begin to distort as soon as they enter the conical die, and continue to distort within the die. A theoretical field solution for this deformation problem has not yet been obtained, although many slip line field solutions exist for the analogous two dimensional plane strain problem (of extruding a wide sheet). What has generally been done in the past is to *assume* a deformation pattern for the material and calculate the associated stresses and strains. This was originally done by Siebel[55] for the wire drawing process.

(iii) *Friction work*

In hydrostatic extrusion, friction is substantially eliminated between the billet and the main container wall. Some friction must still occur between the die and the material passing through it, since they are in close proximity. In the case of a conical die with a cylindrical extension (land) as shown in Fig. 14, friction is assumed to occur along these surfaces (Γ_3 and Γ_4 respectively). Generally, one of two alternative friction conditions may be assumed, namely Coulomb friction in which the surface shear stress τ is proportional to the surface pressure q through the friction coefficient μ, so that $\tau = \mu q$, or the surface

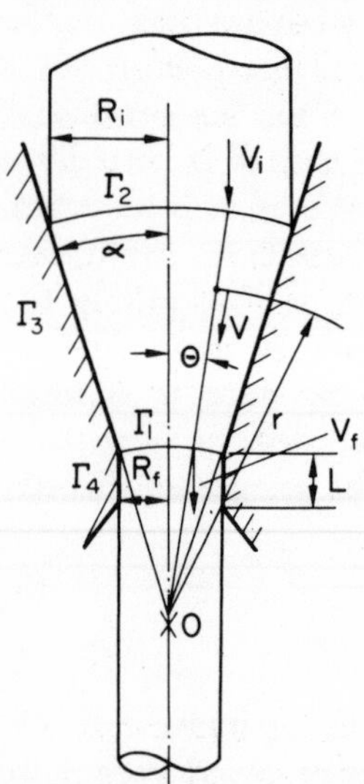

Fig. 14. Kinematically admissable velocity field in the conical die. (After Avitzur, Ref. 58.)

shear stress τ is constant at some value less than the shear yield stress of the material k (assumed constant), so that $\tau = mk$ where the constant $m < 1$. Several investigators, notably Hillier[60] for the hydrostatic extrusion process, have endeavoured to analyse metal-working processes on the assumption that hydrodynamic conditions exist in the fluid or lubricant present between the work and tool surfaces.

It has been proved by Hill[56] and Prager and Hodge[57] that, provided a chosen deformation pattern is kinematically admissible, it will give an upper bound value of the loads required. Similarly, a statically admissible stress field will give a lower bound value of the loads required. In practice, it is much easier to envisage kinematically admissible velocity fields than statically admissible stress fields, so this is usually done. These techniques are usually referred to as limit analysis, although the required lower bounds are rarely estimated. A kinematically admissible velocity field is simply a deformation pattern which satisfies the velocity boundary conditions and compatibility of velocities and strains within the material. In the case of hydrostatic extrusion, the material must enter and leave the die with the correct velocities and move through the conical confines of the die in an acceptable way. A statically admissible stress field is a pattern of stresses which are in equilibrium throughout the material and the boundary loads, such that the material is everywhere either at or below the yielding condition.

3.2 UPPER BOUND SOLUTION

Using a kinematically admissible velocity field of the form shown in Fig. 14, in which Γ_1 and Γ_2 are spherical surfaces (centred at the apex 0) in the material across which velocity discontinuities exist, and Γ_3 and Γ_4 are the conical and cylindrical surfaces of the die, Avitzur[58] has derived analytical expressions for the pressure in orthodox hydrostatic extrusion. The material within the conical portion of the die is assumed to move towards the apex of the cone 0.

Avitzur gives the following equation for the upper bound estimate of the pressure required, assuming a constant flow stress σ_0, the yield criterion of Maxwell (von Mises) and Coulomb friction coefficient μ (using Avitzur's notation)

$$\frac{\sigma_{xb}}{\sigma_0} = \frac{\sigma_{xf}}{\sigma_0} + 2f(\alpha) \ln \frac{R_i}{R_f} + \frac{2}{\sqrt{3}}\left(\frac{\alpha}{\sin^2 \alpha} - \cot \alpha\right)$$

$$+ 2\mu\left[\cot\alpha\left(1 + \frac{\sigma_{xf}}{\sigma_0} + \ln\frac{R_i}{R_f}\right)\ln\frac{R_i}{R_f} + \left(1 + \frac{\sigma_{xf}}{\sigma_0}\right)\frac{L}{R_f}\right] \quad (4)$$

where σ_{xb} = pressure in high pressure chamber, σ_{xf} = pressure in low pressure chamber (back pressure)

$$f(\alpha) = \frac{1}{\sin^2 \alpha}\Bigg\{1 - (\cos\alpha)\sqrt{1 - \tfrac{11}{12}\sin^2\alpha}$$

$$+ \frac{1}{\sqrt{11 \times 12}} \ln \frac{1 + \sqrt{\tfrac{11}{12}}}{\sqrt{\tfrac{11}{12}}\cos\alpha + \sqrt{1 - \tfrac{11}{12}\sin^2\alpha}}\Bigg\} \quad (5)$$

and the other symbols are as indicated in Fig. 14.

It will be seen from this equation that Avitzur's analysis is general, for fluid-to-fluid extrusion. The function $f(\alpha)$ represents the factor by which the hypothetical extrusion pressure of equation (3) must be multiplied to include the redundant work which occurs for the particular velocity field assumed within the conical portion of the die. The term

$$\frac{2}{\sqrt{3}}\left(\frac{\alpha}{\sin^2 \alpha} - \cot \alpha\right)$$

in equation (4) represents the redundant work done when the material passes across the two spherical surfaces of velocity discontinuity and the last term represents the work done against friction along the conical surface of the die and the cylindrical surface of the die land. The analysis is based on the assumption of a velocity field within the conical die of

$$v = -v_f r_f^2 \frac{\cos\theta}{r^2}$$

which satisfies the required boundary conditions along the

die surface and at the spherical entry and exit surfaces, viz. the condition of volume constancy

$$\pi R_i^2 v_i = \pi R_f^2 v_f$$

Avitzur has also considered the frictional condition of constant shear stress along the die-material interface, deriving a similar expression.* He used his theory to determine the optimum die angle under given conditions and to try and predict the die angle at which a dead metal zone will be formed, on the assumption that this zone also forms a conical surface. An optimum die angle exists at which the extrusion pressure is a minimum because the smaller the angle the larger the frictional loss, whilst the larger the angle the larger the loss due to redundant work.

Pugh[5] has adopted a similar approach, but considered various shapes of boundary (Γ_1 and in Γ_2 Fig. 14), calculating the redundant work for these boundaries and comparing them to find the smallest. He examines a plane transverse boundary, a conical boundary and a spherical boundary (for which he derives the same result as Avitzur). The minimum redundant work is given by the conical boundary provided its angular span is optimised, but since the difference is small for small die angles (only 6% at 120° included die angle), he uses the spherical boundary in the subsequent analysis. Unlike Avitzur he neglects the contribution to redundant work actually made within the conical die, and follows Hoffman and Sachs[59] by assuming homogeneous deformation there. In view of the fact that $f(\alpha)$ of equation (5) is very nearly unity for small values of α this is a reasonable assumption.

Pugh also makes some allowance for work hardening

* For constant shear stress ($\tau = mk$), Avitzur derives the expression:

$$\frac{\sigma_{xb}}{\sigma_0} = \frac{\sigma_{xf}}{\sigma_0} + 2f(\alpha)\ln\frac{R_i}{R_f} + \frac{2}{\sqrt{3}}\left\{\frac{\alpha}{\sin^2\alpha} - \cot\alpha + m\left[(\cot\alpha)\ln\frac{R_i}{R_f} + \frac{L}{R_f}\right]\right\} \qquad (4a)$$

during passage of the material through the die by considering the magnitude of the strain suffered at each stage of the process and using that part of the yield–stress curve associated with those particular strain limits. He also derives a simple expression for friction on the conical die surface by assuming a mean normal die pressure there and does not consider the die land. His final expression is

$$p = \int_0^{\varepsilon_3} Y\,d\varepsilon + \frac{\mu R \ln R}{(R-1)\sin\alpha}\int_{\varepsilon_1}^{\varepsilon_2} Y\,d\varepsilon \qquad (6)$$

where

$$\varepsilon_1 = 0{\cdot}462\left(\frac{\alpha}{\sin^2\alpha} - \cot\alpha\right)$$

$$\varepsilon_2 = \varepsilon_1 + \ln R$$

$$\varepsilon_3 = \varepsilon_1 + \varepsilon_2 = 2\varepsilon_1 + \ln R$$

In these equations Y is the (variable) yield or flow stress, ε_1 is the redundant (true) strain in crossing the entry and exit spherical boundary (note that Pugh replaces Avitzur's theoretical value of $1/\sqrt{3} = 0{\cdot}577$ by the value of 0·462 to give better agreement with his experimentally determined values of redundant work), ε_2 is the total (true) strain suffered before crossing the exit boundary, ε_3 is the final total strain, and R is the extrusion ratio.

Although not immediately apparent, equation (6) does show a minimum. For a given friction coefficient μ and low die angle α the second term predominates, whilst for a large die angle the first term increases since the integral is taken over a larger strain, determined by the redundant strain ε_1. If a constant yield stress σ_0 is assumed, Pugh's equation 6 can be integrated to give

$$p = \sigma_0\varepsilon_3 + \frac{\mu R \ln R \sigma_0}{(R-1)\sin\alpha}(\varepsilon_2 - \varepsilon_1)$$

or

$$\frac{p}{\sigma_0} = 0{\cdot}924\left(\frac{\alpha}{\sin^2\alpha} - \cot\alpha\right) + \ln R + \frac{\mu R(\ln R)^2}{(R-1)\sin\alpha} \qquad (7)$$

Equation (7) shows more readily the existence of a minimum value of p with respect to variation of α.

In practice, high strain rates usually occur in hydrostatic extrusion and these lead to adiabatic heating, both of which factors affect the flow stress of the material. Thus it hardly seems worthwhile including an allowance for strain hardening, since the effect is likely to be offset by strain rate and heating effects. In the circumstances it seems adequate and in fact desirable to assume a constant yield or flow stress σ_0, as was done by Avitzur.

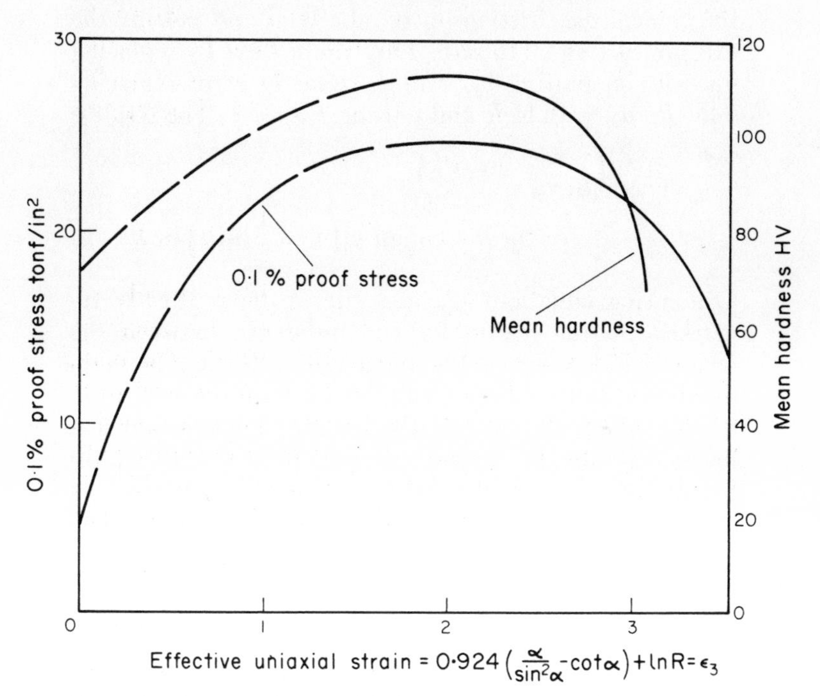

Fig. 15. Mean hardness and 0·1% proof stress of hydrostatically extruded electrolytic tough pitch high conductivity copper. (*After Lengyel* et al., *Ref. 61.*)

This conclusion is substantiated by the work of Lengyel and Culver.[61] The hardness and 0·1 % proof stress of the hydrostatically extruded copper showed a maximum and then decreased with increasing extrusion ratio owing to thermal softening (Fig. 15). Similar results were obtained by Thompson[62] and Herø and Mikkelsen[50] for aluminium. Duffill and Mellor[44] found that their experimental results apparently predicted smaller and smaller amounts of redundant and friction work as the reduction ratio (and hence adiabatic heating effects) increased. This was probably because their "homogeneous work" curve was derived from the static stress-strain curve for the material.

It is interesting to rewrite Avitzur's equation (4) using Pugh's notation and neglecting redundant work within the conical die, friction on the die land and putting the exit pressure equal to zero. This can be done by replacing σ_{xb} with p, putting σ_{xf} and L equal to zero, replacing $2 \ln (R_i/R_f)$ with $\ln R$ and putting $f(\alpha) = 1$. The result is

$$\frac{p}{\sigma_0} = \frac{2}{\sqrt{3}}\left(\frac{\alpha}{\sin^2 \alpha} - \cot \alpha\right) + \ln R + \mu(\cot \alpha)\left(1 + \frac{1}{2} \ln R\right) \ln R \quad (8)$$

Comparing equations (7) and (8) we have already remarked on the reason for the difference between the factors $0{\cdot}924 = 2 \times 0{\cdot}462$ and $1{\cdot}115 = 2/\sqrt{3}$. The main difference in the theories is in the last terms derived from friction along the conical die surface. Pugh assumed a mean constant die pressure derived from overall equilibrium conditions whilst Avitzur assumed a variable die pressure decreasing towards the exit (after Sachs). The factors $\mu \cot \alpha = \dfrac{\mu}{\tan \alpha}$ and $\dfrac{\mu}{\sin \alpha}$ in the last terms of these equations will be almost equal for small die angles, but the factor $\dfrac{R}{R-1} (\ln R)^2$ is very different from the factor $(1 + \frac{1}{2} \ln R) \ln R$ as illustrated in Table 1.

It is unfortunate that these two theories, each based on reasonable assumptions, should give such different results for this friction term. The factors $\mu \cot \alpha$ and $\dfrac{\mu}{\sin \alpha}$ in the respective theories do, however, both confirm the fact that the die angle should not be too small, since there must always be some friction present on the die and this will lead to a significant contribution to the extrusion pressure.

Table 1.

R	1	10	100	1000
$\frac{R}{R-1}(\ln R)^2$ (Pugh)	0	5·873	21·43	47·79
$(1+\frac{1}{2}\ln R)\ln R$ (Avitzur)	0	4·955	15·216	30·78

3.3 HYDRODYNAMIC THEORY

Hillier[60] has based his analysis on the velocity field proposed by Avitzur and postulated a surface shear stress due to viscous shearing of the lubricant given approximately by the equation

$$\tau = \frac{\eta v}{H}$$

where η is the lubricant viscosity, v the velocity of the material at any point on the surface and H is the thickness of the fluid at that point (assumed constant along the die). This leads to an expression of the form (using Avitzur's notation)

$$\frac{\sigma_{xb}}{\sigma_0} = \frac{2}{\sqrt{3}}\left(\frac{\alpha}{\sin^2\alpha} - \cot\alpha\right) + 2f(\alpha)\ln\frac{R_i}{R_f} + \sqrt{N\frac{2r}{(1-r)^{3/2}}\frac{f(\alpha)\cos^2\alpha}{\sin\alpha}} \quad \text{(after Hillier)} \qquad (9)$$

where r is the fractional reduction $1-\left(\frac{R_f}{R_i}\right)^2$, and N is a "modified" Sommerfeld number $\frac{\eta v_i}{\sigma_0 R_i}$

There seems to be a small error in Hillier's analysis in his equation $\frac{dr_2}{dH_0} = -1$. This should, in our opinion, be $\frac{dr_2}{dH_0} = -\sec\alpha$. Such a change gives the last term in equation (9) as

$$\sqrt{N\frac{2r}{(1-r)^{3/2}}f(\alpha)\cot\alpha}$$

that is, it differs by the factor cos α which will be approximately unity for small α.

By taking Pugh's experimental results[64] for an aluminium alloy and deducting Avitzur's theoretical estimate for frictionless extrusion (but including redundant work), Hillier determines a value of N and shows that it is not unreasonable under certain conditions. He concludes that a form of dimensionless Sommerfeld number can be used to indicate by its magnitude whether or not hydrodynamic lubrication will exist and postulates that there are at least four possible interfacial conditions: (*a*) hydrodynamic lubrication, (*b*) partial boundary lubrication, (*c*) full boundary lubrication (probably associated with Coulomb friction conditions) and (*d*) a regime in which a dead metal zone is formed.

These seem to be the main attempts to develop theories for *orthodox hydrostatic extrusion*, although the work by Lambert and Kobayashi[63] should be mentioned here. In essence they achieve more realistic (lower) upper bound solutions for axisymmetric extrusion by superimposing basic flow patterns of the type already discussed, but with more complicated shapes of entry and exit velocity discontinuities spread over a band, thereby giving a theoretical deformation pattern closely resembling experiment. Their solutions have to be determined numerically, the shape of the entry and exit boundaries to the deformation zone being found by minimising the energy of deformation. Their theoretical solutions give extrusion pressures which closely follow the empirical equation (10) given below and they tabulate values of a and b for a range of die angles and friction conditions.

To summarise, the main difference between these theories lies in the method of allowing for friction along the die surface. In practice, as will be shown later, the well-known empirical equation used for conventional extrusion, namely

$$\frac{p}{\sigma_0} = a + b \ln R \tag{10}$$

fits the few experimental results which exist for hydrostatic extrusion. Looking again at equations (4), (7) and (9) we see that if the terms involving the reduction are removed from each equation we are left with the single expression

$$\frac{2}{\sqrt{3}}\left(\frac{\alpha}{\sin^2 \alpha} - \cot \alpha\right)$$

representing the redundant work in crossing the entry and exit velocity discontinuities which may therefore be regarded as giving an estimate of the constant a in equation (10). (As previously remarked Pugh has replaced the value $\frac{2}{\sqrt{3}} = 1{\cdot}155$ with $0{\cdot}924$ to obtain better agreement with his experimental results.)

The value of b in equation (10) appears to be dependent on a number of factors, according to these theories, in particular the reduction itself. The die angle α is also a factor, as well as some parameter such as the Coulomb friction coefficient μ, the constant m, or the fluid viscosity η, specifying the frictional conditions between material and die. In view of the difficulty of knowing these frictional conditions and of allowing for the effect on the flow stress of strain, strain rate and temperature, it will undoubtedly be necessary for us to be satisfied with the empirical formula (10) based on experimental data for some time to come.

3.4 THEORIES OF AUGMENTED HYDROSTATIC EXTRUSION AND FLUID-TO-FLUID EXTRUSION

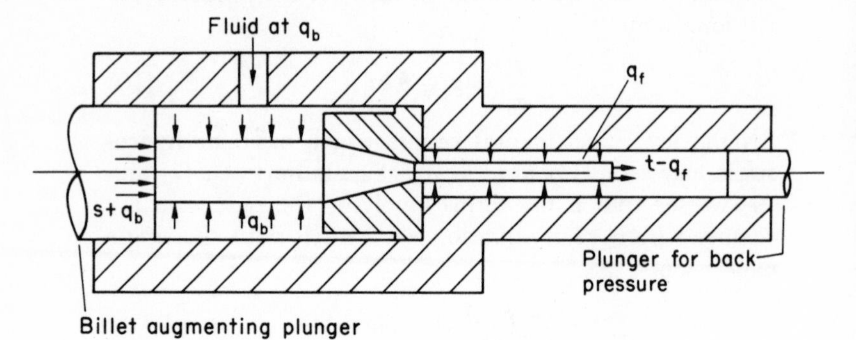

Fig. 16. Augmented hydrostatic extrusion with push and pull into back-pressure.

In fluid-to-fluid extrusion both billet and product are surrounded by fluid at different pressures. Augmentation of the extrusion force can be achieved either by an additional push applied to the billet or by an additional pull applied to the product. The reason for extruding into a fluid at high pressure is to inhibit fracture, whilst the reason for augmentation by pushing or pulling is to reduce the fluid pressure required for extrusion and improve control. The actual system used depends on the material being extruded. Fluid-to-fluid extrusion is attractive for brittle materials, for example. To estimate the effect on the process of these various additional stresses it seems best to use Avitzur's theory which already applies to fluid-to-fluid extrusion.

Let q_b = fluid pressure surrounding the billet (Fig. 16).
q_f = fluid pressure surrounding the product.
s = compressive stress superimposed on the billet.
t = tensile stress superimposed on the product.
p = effective extrusion pressure.

Then, in Avitzur's theory

$$\left.\begin{aligned}\sigma_{xb} &= q_b + s\\ \sigma_{xf} &= q_f - t\end{aligned}\right\} \qquad (11)$$

Thus equation (4) becomes

$$\frac{q_b + s}{\sigma_0} = \frac{q_f - t}{\sigma_0} + 2f(\alpha)\ln\frac{R_i}{R_f} + \frac{2}{\sqrt{3}}\left(\frac{\alpha}{\sin^2\alpha} - \cot\alpha\right)$$

$$+ 2\mu\left[\cot\alpha\left(1 + \frac{q_f - t}{\sigma_0} + \ln\frac{R_i}{R_f}\right) + \left(1 + \frac{q_f - t}{\sigma_0}\right)\frac{L}{R_f}\right] \quad (12)$$

where $f(\alpha)$ is given by equation (5).

The "effective" extrusion pressure is clearly

$$p = q_b - q_f + s + t \quad (13)$$

It can be seen from this equation that if we are dealing with billet augmentation only, so that $q_f = t = 0$, whatever stress s is superimposed on to the back end of the billet the fluid pressure surrounding it can be correspondingly reduced. Provided the sum $q_b + s$ equals the value originally specified for the fluid pressure (σ_{xb}) then extrusion will take place. In practice, this cannot be true because at some point either the lubrication conditions associated with hydrostatic extrusion will break down or else the billet will be upset excessively or buckle.

The effect of product augmentation on its own can be seen by putting $q_f = s = 0$. We then see that the fluid pressure on the billet can be reduced approximately by the amount of the applied tensile stress t (neglecting the friction term at the end of the equation). This is a very attractive proposition because the product has a small area, so that only a small pulling force is required to reduce the fluid pressure on the billet by a large amount. Since this fluid pressure is usually generated by pushing in a plunger equal to the container bore diameter, a considerable reduction in the force on this plunger results from this small force applied to pull the product. The addition of fluid pressure q_f to the product necessitates a roughly corresponding increase to the fluid pressure q_b on the billet, neglecting its effect on the friction term.

Limiting conditions for the cases of billet and product augmentation have been considered by Thompson.[43] In the case of product augmentation, the limiting drawing stress t which can be applied to the product is its yield strength. If the "tag" (or initial length of product to which the pull is applied) has been produced by extrusion then a graphical construction can be used to find the maximum extrusion ratio achievable by product augmentation. This is illustrated in Fig. 17, which relates to the case of product augmentation only, i.e. $q_f = s = 0$ in equations (11) and (12). The fluid pressure q_b surrounding the billet is shown by the broken line, and the stress-strain curve of the material $\bar{\sigma} = H(\bar{\varepsilon}) = H(\ln R)$ is superimposed on this level of fluid pressure. If the tag was extruded through an extrusion ratio R_t its yield strength will be approximately equal to $\bar{\sigma}_t$ as illustrated on the diagram, and this equals $t_{\max}$, the maximum tensile stress which can be applied to the product. As already shown, the "effective" extrusion pressure in the case of augmented fluid-to-fluid extrusion is given by equation (13). The value of this pressure can be determined from equation (12) based on Avitzur's theory or from the other theories outlined earlier. It is sufficiently accurate to assume

$$\frac{p}{Y_m} = a + b \ln R,$$

where Y_m is a mean yield stress, and most experimental results for simple hydrostatic extrusion yield a straight line relationship between p and $\ln R$ of the form

$$p = a' + b' \ln R \tag{14}$$

where a' and b' are constants.

If it be assumed that frictional conditions in the die are not affected by the way in which the effective extrusion pressure p is generated (i.e. by the relative magnitudes of q_b, q_f, s and t in equation (13) the line representing equation (14) can be taken to apply to this case also. The limiting extrusion ratio $R_{\max(t)}$ is then determined by the abscissa corresponding to

$$p_{\max} = q_b + t_{\max} \tag{15}$$

as shown in Fig. 17.

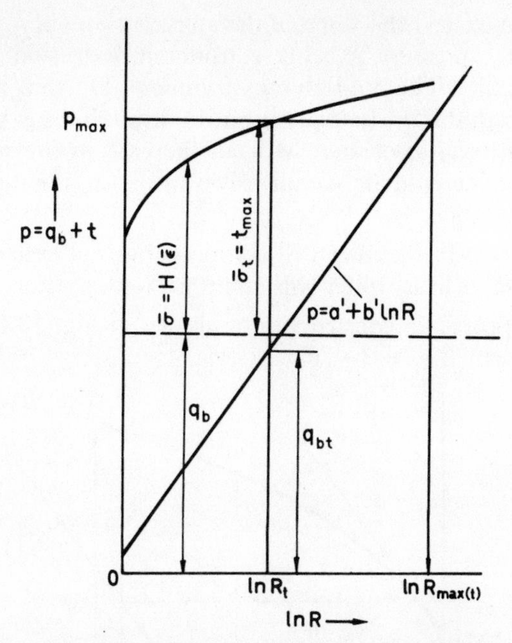

Fig. 17. Limiting conditions in product augmentation.

In practice the value of q_b is limited by the container design so that if the tag is extruded hydrostatically in the same container then the pressure which can be used to extrude the tag will be q_{bt} which must not exceed q_b. Thus the extrusion ratio for the tag cannot exceed R_t. To achieve $R_{\max(t)}$ the tag must apparently be formed from a length of billet which has been machined to a smaller diameter in order to enable extrusion of the tag through the small die which will give $R_{\max(t)}$ on the main billet diameter.

Considering billet augmentation, the billet can fail either by buckling or by plastic upsetting due to the superimposed compressive stress s. Thompson considers the latter case and states that it was found, in his experimental work, that the billet deformed in a homogeneous manner and such deformation was presumably acceptable. Therefore, he assumed that provided the *rate of increase* of the effective extrusion pressure p with respect to strain does not exceed the slope of the stress/strain curve at the particular pressure p being considered, extrusion would be possible. The underlying argument for this is presumably that if the increase in strain through the extrusion die is $\delta(\ln R)$ associated with an increase in pressure δp and the increase in compressive strain in the billet is $\delta\bar{\varepsilon}$ for δp, then:

if $\delta\bar{\varepsilon} > \delta(\ln R)$ billet will compress but not extrude
if $\delta\bar{\varepsilon} < \delta(\ln R)$ billet will compress and extrude.

The appropriate construction is shown in Fig. 18 for the case in which $q_f = t = 0$.

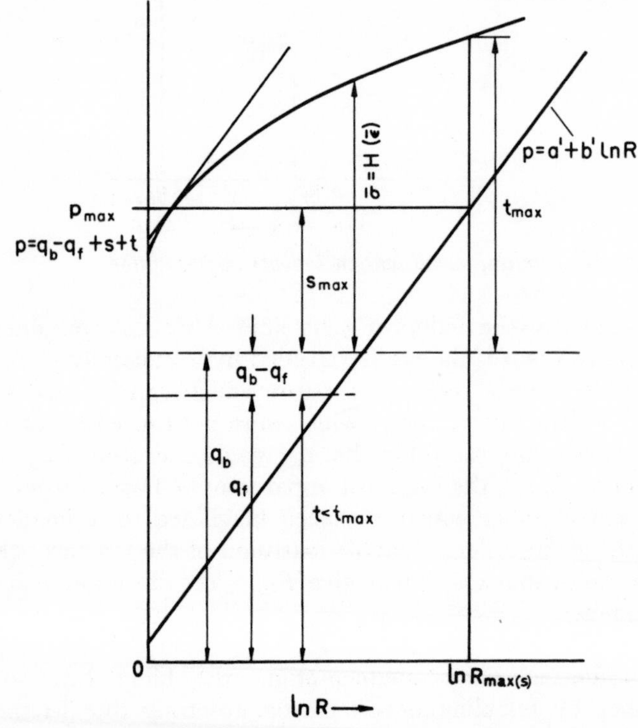

Fig.18. Limiting conditions in hydrostatic extrusion with billet and product augmentation.

It should be noted in this construction that if the billet has been expanded by the strain $\bar{\varepsilon}_{max}$ associated with the maximum augmentation stress s_{max} then the extrusion ratio $R_{max(s)}$ refers to the expanded billet. The maximum extrusion ratio referred to the original billet diameter would be $R_{0max(s)}$ given by the equation:

$$\ln R_{0\ max(s)} = \ln R_{max(s)} - \bar{\varepsilon}_{max} \qquad (16)$$

This is also illustrated in Fig. 19, together with the maximum extrusion ratios for the following cases:

q_b only	R_{max}
$q_b + s$ only	$R_{max(s)}$
$q_b + t$ only	$R_{max(t)}$

It seems from this that, for the typical shape of stress/strain curve shown, product augmentation can provide bigger maximum extrusion ratios than can billet augmentation. However, the problem of forming a tag small enough to pass through the small die associated with $R_{max(t)}$ without machining the billet still remains.

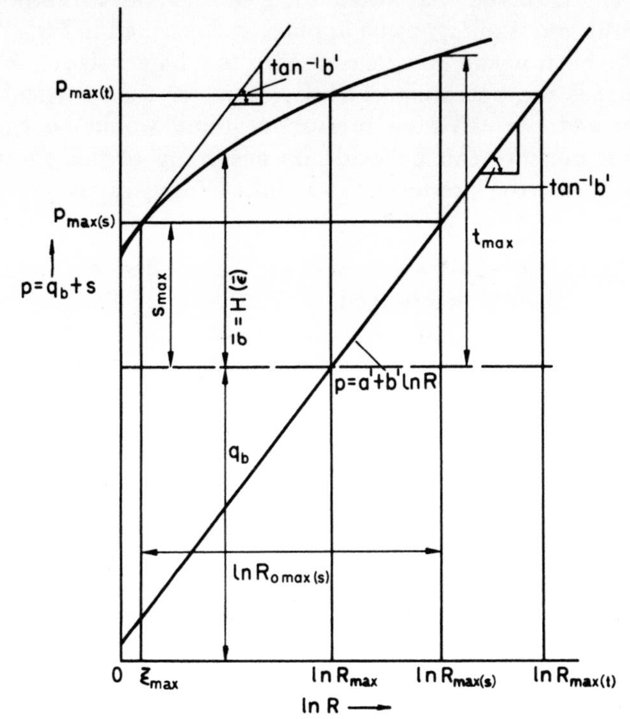

Fig. 19. Limiting conditions in fluid-to-fluid extrusion with billet and product augmentation.

One criticism of the construction giving s_{max} is that the expanded billet will not follow equation (14), which relates to the unexpanded billet. The flatter the stress/strain curve the less will be the error from this cause, and the less will be the difference between the maximum ratios achievable by either method.

In the case of a rounded stress/strain curve of the type shown, it must be remembered that billet expansion due to the augmenting stress can be considerable and the size of the die must be arranged to cater for this.

If the press is such that both s and t can be applied, a possibility would be to extrude the tag using billet augmentation, which would result in an extrusion ratio of $R_{0\,max(s)}$ related to the original billet dimensions. The strength of the tag would then be such as to allow a tensile stress of t_{max} to be applied as illustrated in Fig. 18. The billet would now be expanded to a bigger size so that R_{max} is the operating extrusion ratio for that particular die and the extrusion pressure required would be p_{max}. This pressure can be made up according to this simple theory by the stresses q_b, q_f, s and t in any way to give

$$p_{max} = q_b - q_f + s + t \qquad (13a)$$

provided that s does not exceed s_{max} and t does not exceed t_{max} as already determined. This situation is illustrated in Fig. 19 from which it can be seen that fluid-to-fluid extrusion for quite large extrusion ratios can be achieved provided that both product and billet augmentation can be used. This may be important for brittle materials in which case the stress/strain curve will be flatter and t_{max} will tend to be equal to s_{max}.

All the present discussion has been based on the assumption that augmentation will not affect the frictional conditions in the die. The main experimental investigation of this effect seems to have been that carried out by Parsons, Bretherton and Cole[45] who restricted their attention to product augmentation. Their work showed that as the ratio extrusion stress/drawing stress increased, the friction coefficient increased, reaching a limiting value asymptotically. This effect is attributed to a reduction in the die pressure due to the applied tensile stress, and it can be seen by reference to the last term of equation (2) that the frictional component of the effective extrusion pressure is reduced as t increases, in both the conical and cylindrical parts of the die. The application of an all-round fluid pressure q_f to the product has the reverse effect.

According to equation (12), a superimposed billet augmentation stress s will not have any effect on the frictional component of the effective extrusion pressure. If this were so, it would mean that the whole of the fluid pressure q_b applied to the billet could be replaced by pushing the billet with a load giving a stress s in it, without affecting the frictional conditions in the die. This cannot be true, since the low friction associated with hydrostatic extrusion clearly depends on a supply of high pressure fluid to the billet/die interface. Further work needs to be carried out to investigate these effects experimentally, especially in relation to billet augmentation.

Considering the possibility of buckling of the billet due to billet/augmentation, both ends of the billet may be regarded as fixed, so that the well known elastic Euler buckling load is given by

$$P_{CR} = \frac{4\pi^2 EI}{l^2} \qquad (17)$$

where E = Young's Modulus, l = length of the billet

and I = second moment of area of billet cross-section

$$= \frac{\pi R_i^4}{4}$$

In this particular problem the application of high stresses to the billet is desired, sufficient to cause plastic compression. Therefore the possibility of plastic buckling must be considered. This can be estimated by replacing Young's Modulus E in equation (17) either by the Tangent Modulus E_t or by a Reduced Modulus E_r which is dependent on the sectional shape. In practice, the

Tangent Modulus is easier to use and gives a lower bound which is only slightly below experimentally observed buckling values. This theory was originally proposed by Engesser in 1889.

Rewriting equation (17) in terms of the critical stress for buckling s_{CR} and the Tangent Modulus E_t, we obtain the following equation:

$$\frac{l}{R_i} = \pi\sqrt{\frac{E_t}{s_{CR}}} \tag{18}$$

If it is assumed that any stress on the stress/strain curve is the critical stress for buckling, the critical slenderness ratio l/R_i can be calculated, since the tangent modulus at that stress is known. In this way it is possible to calculate a relationship between s_{CR} and l/R_i. The other limitation on the billet augmentation stress is that it must coincide with a point on the stress/strain curve at which the tangent modulus does not exceed b' (the slope of the effective extrusion pressure versus $\ln R$ relationship); thus the required relationship between s_{CR} and l/R_i over a known range can be calculated.

As an example, consider the case of a mild steel billet. Up to a stress of about 13 tonf/in² the billet will be elastic, and Young's Modulus E can be substituted in place of the Tangent Modulus E_t in equation (18). Thus

$$\frac{l}{R_i} = \pi\sqrt{\frac{13{,}000}{s_{CR}}} \tag{18a}$$

where

$$0 < s_{CR} < 13 \text{ tonf/in}^2$$

This gives a value of $l/R_i \simeq 99{\cdot}3$ when $s_{CR} = 13$ tonf/in² at the point of yielding. l/R_i then decreases until the limiting value is reached at which $E_t = b'$. For mild steel $b' \simeq 45$ tonf/in² and at this point $s_{max} \simeq 36$ tonf/in². Substituting these values in equation (18)

$$\frac{l}{R_i} = \pi\sqrt{\frac{45}{36}} \simeq 3{\cdot}51$$

The form of the relationship between s_{CR} and l/R_i is shown in Fig. 20 for mild steel. For applied stresses above

13 tonf/in² plastic buckling will occur at the values of slenderness ratio l/R_i given in the figure.

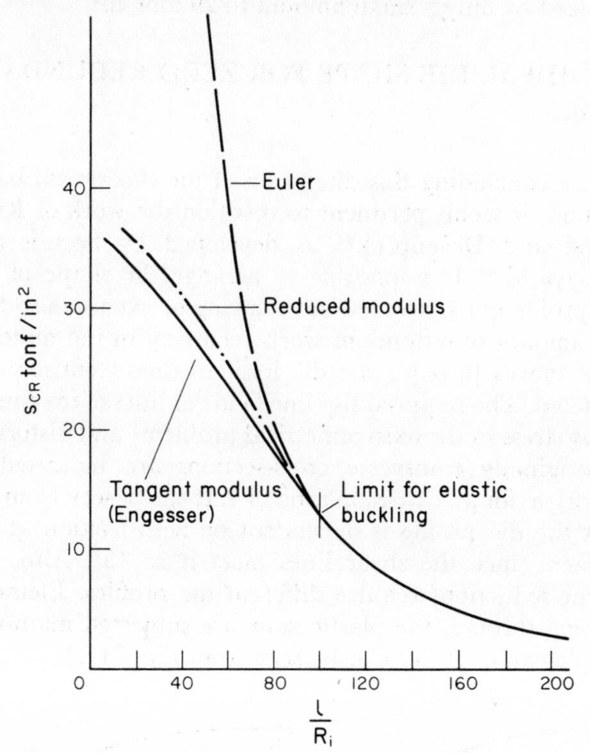

Fig. 20. Plastic buckling behaviour of mild steel.

As an example, consider a billet of mild steel of 2 in diameter (R_i = 1 in). If the limiting billet augmentation stress s_{max} = 36 tonf/in² is applied, l/R_i must not exceed 3·5, i.e. the billet must not exceed 3·5 in in length. As stated previously, the tangent modulus theory is somewhat conservative but this is countered by the fact that we have assumed the billet to be firmly fixed at each end, which may not be true.

It is clear from this that only very short billets can be extruded if the billet augmentation stress approaches the maximum value determined by the rate of expansion of the billet due to plastic compression. Referring again to

Fig. 20, it is possible to extrude a billet length of 40 in without buckling, if the billet augmentation stress is reduced by only a small amount to 29 tonf/in^2.

3.5 IDEAL DIE SHAPE FOR ZERO REDUNDANT WORK

Before concluding this discussion of the theoretical background, it seems pertinent to mention the work of Richmond and Devenpeck[65] as developed by Sortais and Kobayashi.[66] It is possible to arrange the shape of the die profile in axisymmetrical drawing or extrusion so that the amount of redundant work occurring in the material as it moves through the die itself is almost entirely eliminated. The required slip line field (or lines of maximum shear stress in the axisymmetrical problem) and distortion of originally transverse cross-sections are indicated in Fig. 21(a) for an extrusion ratio of 4. It can be seen from this that the die profile is dependent on zero friction at the surface, since the shear lines meet it at 45°. Also, different reductions require different die profiles. Elements passing through the plastic zone are subjected mainly to simple extension, as can be seen from Fig. 21(b).

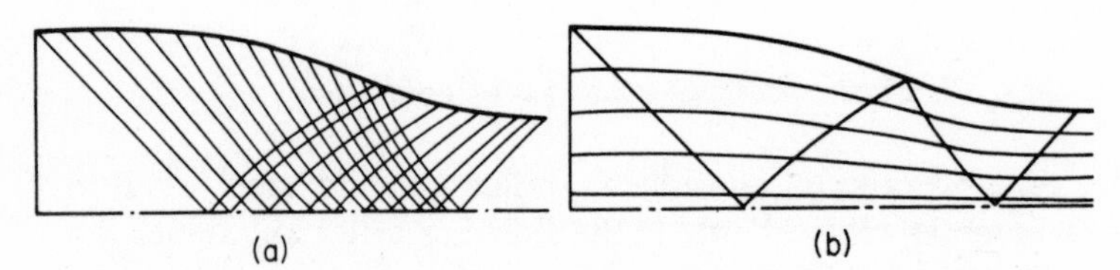

Fig. 21. Slip line field (a) *and flow lines* (b) *for an extrusion ratio of 4.* (*After Sortais* et al., *Ref. 66.*)

Sortais and Kobayashi carried out conventional direct extrusion experiments showing that the efficiency of their curved die (i.e. $\dfrac{\ln R}{p/\sigma_0} \times 100\%$) was 97% as against 43% for a conical die. They used commercially pure lead and a proprietary lubricant containing molybdenum disulphide. On the other hand, they also carried out experiments in which they reduced the billet size and filled up the space between the specimen and the chamber wall with a thick layer of wax, conditions which might be thought to approximate to hydrostatic extrusion. Under those conditions there was little difference between the grid distortion in the curved or conical dies, both exhibiting very little redundant deformation. Since different shapes of curved die would be required for different reductions, it would seem from this that the conical die is to be preferred in hydrostatic extrusion, provided good lubrication can in fact be achieved between die and work-piece.

4. Development of Apparatus

4.1 CONTAINER

The pressure in the hydrostatic extrusion container fluctuates between zero and some peak value, which could be as high as 30 kbar. It is for this reason that, after a discussion of design for static pressures, the fatigue of containers will be considered. This is particularly important for production equipment, when the required life could be 10^5 pressure cycles or more. The discussion will be limited to conditions at room temperature.

4.1.1 *Elastic (non-autofrettaged) Thick Walled Monobloc Cylinders Under Internal Pressure*

Fig. 22 illustrates the cross-section of a thick-walled cylinder and the stresses acting on an element of the material. By symmetry, the hoop stress σ_θ is constant at a given radius and, if the cylinder is long compared with its diameter, there can be no shear stresses in the radial, circumferential and axial directions; thus σ_θ, σ_r and σ_z, the hoop, radial and axial stresses are principal stresses.

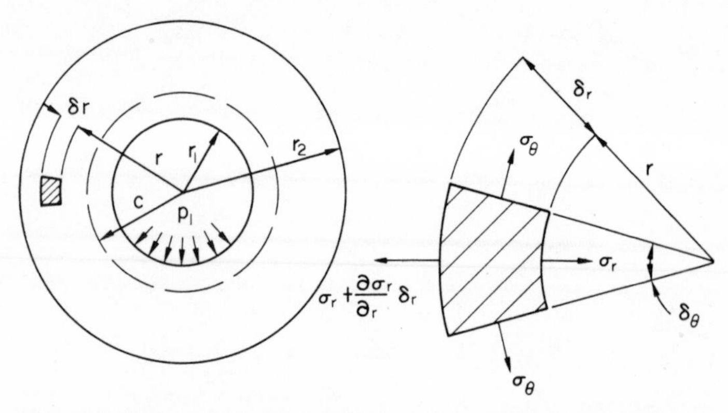

Fig. 22. Stresses in a thick-walled cylinder under internal pressure.

The solution is the Lamé equations which give, for closed ends, with $K = \dfrac{\text{outside radius}}{\text{inside radius}}$ of the cylinder,

$$\sigma_\theta = \frac{p_1}{K^2 - 1} + \frac{p_1 K^2}{K^2 - 1}\left(\frac{r_1}{r}\right)^2 \tag{19}$$

$$\sigma_r = \frac{p_1}{K^2 - 1} - \frac{p_1 K^2}{K^2 - 1}\left(\frac{r_1}{r}\right)^2 \tag{20}$$

$$\sigma_z = \frac{p_1}{K^2 - 1} \tag{21}$$

Thus the stress system is a hydrostatic tension of $\dfrac{p_1}{K^2 - 1}$ superimposed on a pure shear.

The axial stress is the mean principal stress, thus the maximum shear stress is found in the planes of σ_θ and σ_r and its value is

$$\tau_{r\theta} = \frac{p_1 K^2}{K^2 - 1}\left(\frac{r_1}{r}\right)^2 \tag{22}$$

For open ends $\sigma_z = 0$ and the maximum shear stress remains the same.

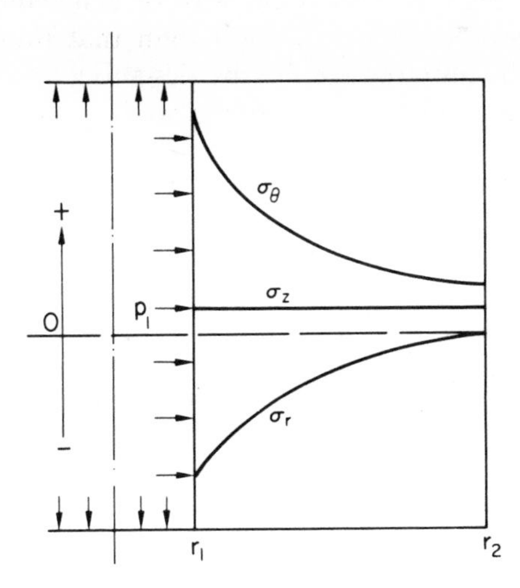

Fig. 23. Stresses in a closed-end thick cylinder.

The stress distribution for the closed end condition is shown in Fig. 23, which indicates that stresses in the inner layers are substantially higher than towards the outside; thus, the material utilisation is poor in the outer layers and first yield occurs in the bore. The Maxwell-von Mises criterion predicts that the yield pressure for closed ends is

$$p_y = \frac{Y}{\sqrt{3}}\left(1 - \frac{1}{K^2}\right) \tag{23}$$

For open ends

$$p_y = \frac{Y}{\sqrt{3}}\left(1 - \frac{1}{K^2}\right)\frac{1}{\sqrt{1 + \frac{1}{3K^4}}} \tag{24}$$

The Tresca yield criterion predicts yield in the bore when

$$p_y = \frac{Y}{2}\left(1 - \frac{1}{K^2}\right) \tag{25}$$

both for open and closed ends.

4.1.2 *Prestressing by Autofrettage*

A monobloc cylinder yields in the bore at a pressure of about 10 kbar, even if it is made from the strongest steel with very high K-ratio. One way of achieving a more advantageous stress distribution than that illustrated in Fig. 23 is by autofrettage, i.e. by designing for controlled plastic deformation in the cylinder wall.

In the approximate analysis it is assumed that the material is non-work hardening and follows the Tresca yield criterion. Then the stresses during autofrettage in the plastic zone ($r_1 \leqslant r \leqslant c$ where c is the plastic-elastic interface radius, Fig. 22)

$$\sigma_\theta = \frac{Y}{2}\left[\left(\frac{c}{r_2}\right)^2 + 1 + 2\ln\frac{r}{c}\right] \tag{26}$$

$$\sigma_r = \frac{Y}{2}\left[\left(\frac{c}{r_2}\right)^2 - 1 + 2\ln\frac{r}{c}\right] \tag{27}$$

In determining these equations, no assumption has been made on end conditions, i.e. these apply to both open and closed ends. But σ_z can be determined only by the application of the stress/strain relations, and it depends therefore on the strain history.[56]

The bore pressure to cause plastic flow at radius c from equation (27) by substituting $r = r_1$

$$p = -\sigma_{r_1} = \frac{Y}{2}\left[1 - \left(\frac{c}{r_2}\right)^2 + 2 \ln \frac{c}{r_1}\right] \tag{28}$$

The radial displacement at r_1 is assumed to be small, i.e. r_1 remains at its initial value during autofrettage. Then, by equations (26) and (27) the stresses can be determined statically, without calculating deformations.

For partial overstrain, the stresses in the elastic region ($c \leqslant r \leqslant r_2$) can be obtained from equations (19) and (20), with c replacing r_1 and p_y from equation (25) replacing p_1.

$$\sigma_\theta = \frac{Y}{2}\left(\frac{c}{r_2}\right)^2\left[1 + \left(\frac{r_2}{r}\right)^2\right] \tag{29}$$

$$\sigma_r = \frac{Y}{2}\left(\frac{c}{r_2}\right)^2\left[1 - \left(\frac{r_2}{r}\right)^2\right] \tag{30}$$

A typical stress distribution is shown in Fig. 24. When the autofrettage pressure is released, the residual stresses can be obtained by calculating the stresses under pressure and subtracting from these the stresses which would be set up if the material were elastic at the autofrettage pressure. The residual stresses for partial overstrain in the elastic zone, from equations (28), (29) and (30)

$$\sigma_\theta = \frac{Y}{2}\left[1 + \left(\frac{r_2}{r}\right)^2\right]\left\{\left(\frac{c}{r_2}\right)^2 - \frac{1}{K^2 - 1}\left[1 - \left(\frac{c}{r_2}\right)^2 + 2 \ln \frac{c}{r_1}\right]\right\} \tag{31}$$

$$\sigma_r = \frac{Y}{2}\left[1 - \left(\frac{r_2}{r}\right)^2\right]\left\{\left(\frac{c}{r_2}\right)^2 - \frac{1}{K^2 - 1}\left[1 - \left(\frac{c}{r_2}\right)^2 + 2 \ln \frac{c}{r_1}\right]\right\} \tag{32}$$

The residual stresses in the plastic zone for partial overstrain can be obtained in a similar manner from equations (26), (27) and (28)

$$\sigma_\theta = \frac{Y}{2}\left\{\left(\frac{c}{r_2}\right)^2 + 1 + 2\ln\frac{r}{c} - \frac{1}{K^2-1}\left[1+\left(\frac{r_2}{r}\right)^2\right]\left[1-\left(\frac{c}{r_2}\right)^2 + 2\ln\frac{c}{r_1}\right]\right\} \quad (33)$$

$$\sigma_r = \frac{Y}{2}\left\{\left(\frac{c}{r_2}\right)^2 - 1 + 2\ln\frac{r}{c} - \frac{1}{K^2-1}\left[1-\left(\frac{r_2}{r}\right)^2\right]\left[1-\left(\frac{c}{r_2}\right)^2 + 2\ln\frac{c}{r_1}\right]\right\} \quad (34)$$

A typical residual stress distribution is shown in Fig. 25.

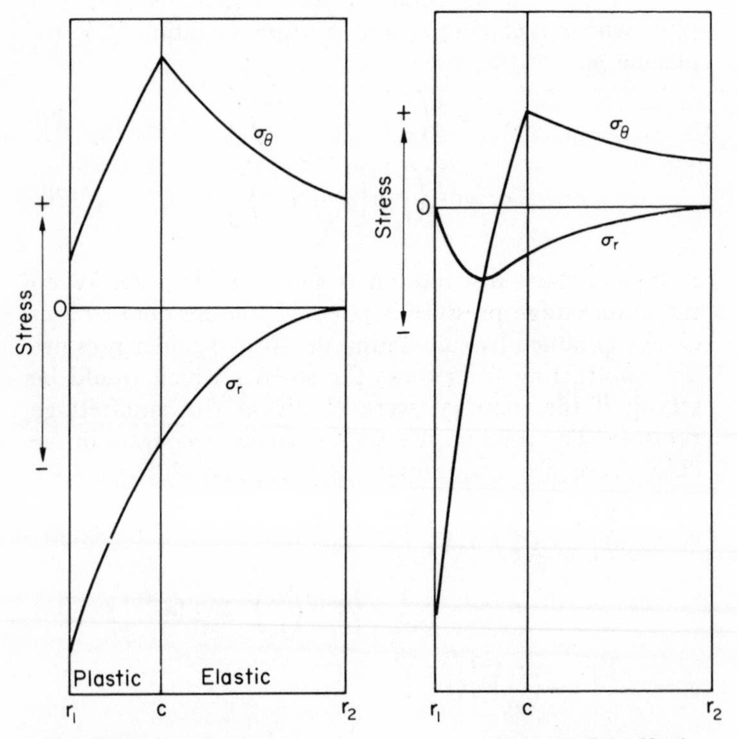

Fig. 24. Stress distribution during autofrettage.

Fig. 25. Distribution of residual stresses.

To cause full overstrain in the cylinder wall, from equation (28) with $c = r_2$

$$p_u = Y \ln K \tag{35}$$

Experiments showed that, if an autofrettaged cylinder is given a low temperature heat treatment at 250°C–350°C, it operates in the elastic manner on subsequent pressurisations below the autofrettage pressure. Consequently the maximum elastic pressure that an autofrettaged cylinder can support is either that given by equation (35) or, if identical tensile and compressive yield strengths are assumed,

$$p_Y = Y\left(1 - \frac{1}{K^2}\right) \tag{36}$$

Equation (35) determines the maximum elastic pressure for $K < 2{\cdot}22$, when the limitation is the burst pressure. If $K > 2{\cdot}22$, then the limitation is reverse yield in the bore and equation (36) is applicable. This indicates that the maximum elastic pressure for a thick-walled autofrettaged cylinder is twice that for a non-autofrettaged cylinder, given by equation (25).

To obtain strains and corresponding stresses for a container made from a work-hardening material, a practical method has been suggested by Nadai[68] and Manning.[69] Here, the treatment given in reference 67 will be followed in brief.

Closed-end cylinder and plane strain conditions are assumed. For this case the Maxwell-von Mises yield criterion becomes $\sigma_\theta - \sigma_r = \frac{2}{\sqrt{3}}Y$, the equation of equilibrium $\frac{d\sigma_r}{dr} = \frac{2}{\sqrt{3}}\frac{Y}{r}$ and the equivalent plastic strain can be written in the form

$$\bar{\varepsilon} = \frac{2}{\sqrt{3}} \ln \frac{r+u}{u} = \frac{1}{\sqrt{3}} \ln \left[1 + \frac{2r_1u_1 + u_1{}^2}{r^2}\right] \tag{37}$$

where r is any radius in the plastic zone, u is the radial displacement at that radius and u_1 is the radial displacement at r_1.

Since $\sigma_r = -p_1$ at $r = r_1$ and zero at $r = r_2$, on integrating the equation of equilibrium the bore pressure is obtained

$$p_1 = \frac{2}{\sqrt{3}} \int_{r_1}^{r_2} \frac{Y}{r} \, dr \tag{38}$$

where Y is some function of the equivalent strain given by (37).

This integral can be solved by dividing the cylinder into a number of concentric annuli. If the strains in each annulus are calculated (which correspond to a particular assumed strain in the cylinder bore) then, if the stress/strain curve of the material is known, the pressure to cause this strain in each annulus can be obtained. The bore pressure in the cylinder (which corresponds to the assumed bore strain) is then obtained by adding the pressures for all annuli

$$p_1 = \frac{2}{\sqrt{3}} \int_{r_1+u_1}^{r_2+u_2} \frac{Y}{r+u} d(r+u) \tag{39}$$

where u, u_1 and u_2 are radial displacements at radii r, r_1 and r_2 respectively.

In evaluating this integral, the value of the yield stress corresponding to the equivalent plastic strain given by equation (37) must be used. In this manner the bore pressure can be obtained for any desired strain, K-ratio and material. For a given material and K-ratio, the curve of bore strain versus bore pressure shows a maximum where bursting of the vessel occurs.

The radial stress distribution under pressure p_1 is then

$$\sigma_r = -p_1 + \frac{2}{\sqrt{3}} \int_{r_1+u_1}^{r+u} \frac{Y}{r+u} \, d(r+u) \tag{40}$$

and the tangential stress distribution

$$\sigma_\theta = \frac{2}{\sqrt{3}} Y + \sigma_r \tag{41}$$

from which the stress distributions for various assumed bore strains may be calculated. The type of stress distribution is similar to that illustrated in Fig. 24.

If elastic release is assumed after the removal of pressure, the residual stresses may be calculated from the conditions under autofrettage pressure and those in the elastic cylinder under pressure, in the manner already described, resulting in a stress distribution similar to that shown in Fig. 25.

Franklin and Morrison found that the measured distribution of residual stresses is different from those calculated on the assumption of elastic release;[70] this difference was as much as 40%. They suggested that the actual behaviour of the cylinder material must be taken into account in the calculations, being best described by the shear stress/strain properties of the material in pure torsion. For an assumed value of shear strain γ_2 on the outside of the cylinder, they calculated the shear strain γ at any radius r, both in the elastic and plastic zones, from the equation

$$\gamma = \gamma_2\left(\frac{r_2}{r}\right)^2 \tag{42}$$

If it is assumed that the axial stress is the intermediate principal stress, then the maximum shear stress $\tau_{r\theta}$ can be obtained from the shear stress/strain curve for each value of the shear strain given by equation (42). By solving the integral

$$p_1 = 2\int_{r_1}^{r_2} \frac{\tau_{r\theta}}{r}\, dr \tag{43}$$

the bore pressure for the assumed outside strain can be obtained. The calculated pressure-strain values can be compared easily with the actual cylinder behaviour by measuring the circumferential and axial strains $e_{\theta 2}$ and e_z on the outside of the cylinder at each pressure, because

$$\gamma_2 = \frac{e_{\theta 2} + \nu e_z}{1 - \nu} \tag{44}$$

where ν is Poisson's ratio.

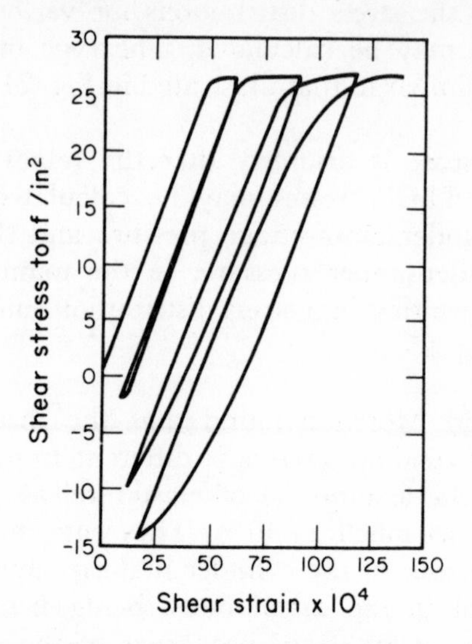

Fig. 26. Shear stress-strain curve determined by the torsion of thin-walled tubes. (After Franklin et al., *Ref. 70.)*

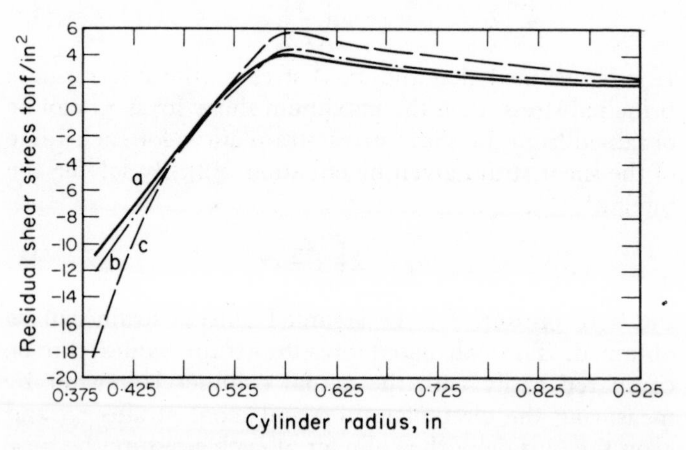

Fig. 27. Residual stresses in a thick cylinder after autofrettage. (After Franklin et al., *Ref. 70)*

a. *Measured.* b. *Calculated by Morrison method.* c. *Calculated from elastic release.*

In calculating the residual stresses, reductions in γ_2 are assumed and corresponding values of γ at several radii are calculated. The corresponding reductions in shear stress are determined from the unloading lines of the stress/strain curve, obtained from torsion tests on thin-walled tubes (Fig. 26). Now equation (43) is evaluated to obtain corresponding reductions in bore pressure. Since the maximum autofrettage pressure and the corresponding strains are known, the release curve can be plotted and for zero bore pressure the reduction in shear stress, thus the residual stresses are found. The calculated distribution of residual stresses agreed well with the measured values (Fig. 27). This method appears suitable to obtain a desired residual stress distribution, an important consideration in the design of thick-walled cylinders not only for static but, as will be shown later, also for cyclic pressures.

4.1.3 *Multi-component Prestressed Compound Pressure Vessels*

Another way of achieving a more advantageous stress distribution in the cylinder wall is by building the vessel from a number of individual layers and assembling them by prestressing to introduce residual stresses. In addition to a more uniform stress distribution and consequent reduction in size and weight, there are further important advantages of the multi-layer prestressed design, such as:

(1) Size effect in heat treatment is reduced, i.e. more uniform mechanical and metallurgical properties of the individual components can be maintained than is possible in the monobloc vessel of much larger wall thickness.

(2) Crack propagation is retarded at the component interfaces, an important safety consideration.

(3) The various components can be made from materials of different properties which can then be best utilised.

(4) The fatigue life of the vessel is improved by introducing compressive pre-stresses into the inner components.

(5) The radial elastic dilatation of the bore under cyclic pressure can be greatly reduced, and sealing becomes easier.

(6) With suitable design, the replacement of the innermost component, the liner, can be made easier. This is important in hydrostatic extrusion containers, when the liner is most likely to fail owing to the effect of the fluid, or possible damage by the billet, or fatigue, etc.

In the following section, only those designs will be discussed which could be particularly useful in the building of hydrostatic extrusion containers, such as:

Compound shrinkage by thermal means and by taper press-fits.
Tape and wire winding.
Static fluid interfacial pressure.
Dynamic support by taper fits.
Dynamic fluid interfacial pressure.

Because none of these designs is usually suitable for supporting end-loads, open-ended conditions only will be considered.

4.1.3.1. *Compound Shrinkage by Thermal Means and by Taper Press-fit*

In compound shrinkage by thermal means, the outside diameter of the liner is made larger than the bore of the supporting cylinder, by the amount of the calculated interference, while both diameters are parallel. A clearance fit is produced at assembly by heating the outer cylinder, by cooling the liner or both. This method of construction can be repeated for the second, third, etc., supporting cylinders to build up a multi-component vessel. The temperature of heating must not exceed the tempering temperature of the material, if a change in material properties is to be avoided and this places a maximum limit on the interference that can be applied by this method. Another limitation is that axial stresses induced during shrinkage are unpredictable and could be significant with the resultant loss in the accuracy of the calculated stresses.[71]

Another method for achieving interference fits is by pressing together the components at room temperature, by the application of an axial load, with mating surfaces machined to a small taper, usually 1°–2° included angle, and with the required interference. The limitation in this case is the maximum compressive stress that the components can support during assembly without yielding. This difficulty can be reduced by making the outer cylinders from shorter rings, as illustrated in Fig. 28; this would decrease end loads and manufacturing costs.

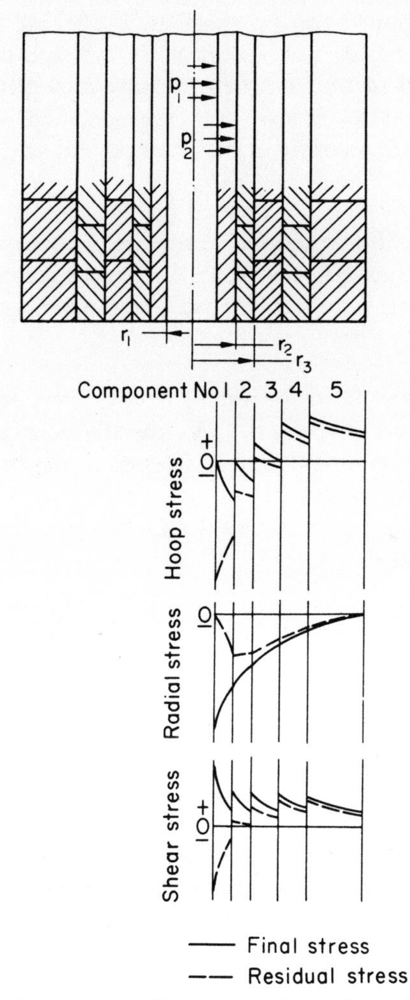

Fig. 28. Shrink or taper fit compound container. (*After Lengyel* et al., *Ref. 30.*)

Both the shrink and press-fit constructions suffer from the discrepancy between the specified interference and those actually produced in the assembly (contribution to Ref. 30).

In the optimum design, i.e. when the material is best utilised, all components are designed to yield simultaneously. Alternatively, the permissible stresses at the working pressure can be specified by taking a factor of safety into consideration, separately for each component. The method of optimisation for simultaneous yield can then be used to ensure that the specified stresses are reached simultaneously in each component at the required pressure.

One optimisation method[72] uses the Tresca yield criterion with the assumption that the axial stresses are intermediate at all points in the wall of the multi-component cylinder.

Let p_1 be the fluid pressure in the bore of the liner (Fig. 28) and $K_1, K_2 \ldots, K_n$ the diameter ratios, $Y_1, Y_2, \ldots, Y_n$ the uniaxial yield stresses in the first, second, $\ldots$, n^{th} component then, at simultaneous yield the maximum bore pressure that can be contained is given by the equation

$$(p_1)_{\max} = \frac{1}{2}(Y_1+Y_2+\ldots+Y_n) - \frac{n}{2}\left(\frac{Y_1Y_2\ldots Y_n}{K^2}\right)^{\frac{1}{n}} \quad (45)$$

and

$$\frac{Y_1}{K_1^2} = \frac{Y_2}{K_2^2} = \ldots = \frac{Y_n}{K_n^2} \quad (46)$$

where $K_1.K_2\ldots K_n = K$ is the overall diameter ratio.

From these equations the overall diameter ratio K and that of the individual components can be computed at the required values of yield stress and bore pressure, but the interference between the components must still be determined.

To obtain interface pressures $p_2, p_3 \ldots p_n$ while p_1 is acting, it is assumed that the shear stress given by equation (22) is the critical stress and is given.

Then the bore shear stresses in components 1, 2, . . ., n

are

$$\left.\begin{aligned} \tau_1 &= (p_1 - p_2)\frac{K_1^2}{K_1^2 - 1} \\ \tau_2 &= (p_2 - p_3)\frac{K_2^2}{K_2^2 - 1} \\ \tau_n &= p_n\frac{K_n^2}{K_n^2 - 1} \end{aligned}\right\} \tag{47}$$

If the diameter ratios are obtained from equation (46) the interface pressures can be determined from equation (47).

Now the residual interface pressures p_{2r}, p_{3r}, etc. produced by the interference between the components, can be determined. For example, in the liner, the radial stress that would act in a monobloc cylinder of the same dimensions as the compound vessel must be calculated at the radius equal to the interface radius between the first and second cylinders and subtracted from p_2

$$p_{2r} = p_2 - p_1\frac{K^2 - K_1^2}{K_1^2(K^2 - 1)} \tag{48}$$

The amount of interference between components 1 and 2 can be calculated by adding the amount by which the liner outside diameter is reduced by the application of p_{2r} to the amount by which the bore of the second component expands as a result of p_{2r} acting in that bore and p_{3r} on its outside.

When the pressure is very high, compound vessels with tool steel or tungsten carbide liners can be built, to extend the elastic range of operation. The compressive strength of these materials is high, but they can support little or no tensile stress. If the cylinder is open-ended, the only tensile stress likely to occur is in the tangential direction. For tungsten carbide which has very small tensile strength, the usual criterion is that $\sigma_\theta \leqslant 0$. In the bore of the liner, if p_2 is the interface pressure (Ref. 69)

$$-p_2K_1^2 + p_1 - p_2K_1^2 + p_1K_1^2 \leqslant 0$$

and

$$p_2 \geqslant p_1\frac{K_1^2 + 1}{2K_1^2} \tag{49}$$

The other design limitation is that the residual stress must not cause failure of the liner in compression. If Y_c is the compressive strength of the liner then

$$p_{2r} \leqslant Y_c\frac{K_1^2 - 1}{2K_1^2} \tag{50}$$

The radial dilatation of the liner and the outer cylinder under pressure p_1 must be equal. This condition gives the difference at r_2 between the residual interface pressure and that when p_1 is acting:

$$\left.\begin{aligned} p_2 - p_{2r} &= p_1\frac{2\alpha_2}{\alpha_1\alpha_2 + \alpha_3\alpha_4} \\ \text{where } \alpha_1 &= K_1^2(1 - \nu_1) + (1 + \nu_1) \\ \alpha_2 &= \frac{1}{E_1(K_1^2 - 1)} \\ \alpha_3 &= K_2^2(1 + \nu_2) + (1 - \nu_2) \\ \alpha_4 &= \frac{1}{E_2(K_2^2 - 1)} \end{aligned}\right\} \tag{51}$$

Here E is Young's modulus, ν Poisson's ratio and indices 1 and 2 refer to the liner and supporting cylinder respectively.

To illustrate one possible benefit that can be achieved by this construction, consider a tungsten carbide liner of $K_1 = 1{\cdot}75$, $E_1 = 89 \times 10^6$ lbf/in², $\nu_1 = 0{\cdot}25$, $Y_c = 220$ tonf/in² supported by a steel cylinder of $K_2 = 3$, $E_2 = 30 \times 10^6$ lbf/in², $\nu_2 = 0{\cdot}29$ and $Y_2 = 100$ tonf/in². By using the limiting values of equations (49) and (50), this assembly can support a maximum elastic pressure of

21 kbar against 15·4 kbar and 7·7 kbar for an elastic monobloc cylinder with and without autofrettage, made from the same steel to $K = 1{\cdot}75 \times 3 = 5{\cdot}25$ (equations 25 and 36).

It has been mentioned that equations (45), (46) and (47) are valid only if σ_z is the intermediate principal stress. This is clearly not the case if, in an open-ended multi-component cylinder, the innermost component is pre-stressed in such a manner that σ_θ is compressive at the maximum bore pressure. However, the thickness of the liner in such cases is usually decided from manufacturing considerations and, once the interface pressure between the liner and the first supporting cylinder is found, equation (45) to (47) can be used to obtain the optimum design for the supporting cylinders.

4.1.3.2. *Tape and Wire Winding*

To obtain the calculated residual stresses in the components of a compound shrink or taper fit cylinder requires great manufacturing accuracy which is difficult to achieve. An alternative method of making a vessel for large pressures is by winding tape or wire on to the outside of a monobloc or multi-component cylinder, when the number of interfaces which must be accurately machined is low (Fig. 29). That crack propagation in the windings is likely to be more effectively retarded than in all previously discussed designs, is an important safety consideration.

For optimum design, under bore pressure p_1, the direct stress in the liner can be limited to a predetermined value Y and the hoop stress in the winding σ_θ kept constant also at a predetermined value. If r is any radius in the winding, r_1 is the bore radius of the liner and r_2 is the interface radius between winding and liner (Fig. 29), then the wire tension during winding is given by (Ref. 73)

$$t = \frac{p_1 - \sigma_\theta}{r^2 - r_1^2}\left\{\frac{r_2}{r}(r^2 + r_1^2) - 2r_1^2\right\} - \frac{(r_2^2 - r_1^2)(r^2 + r_1^2)Y}{2r_2 r(r^2 - r_1^2)} \qquad (52)$$

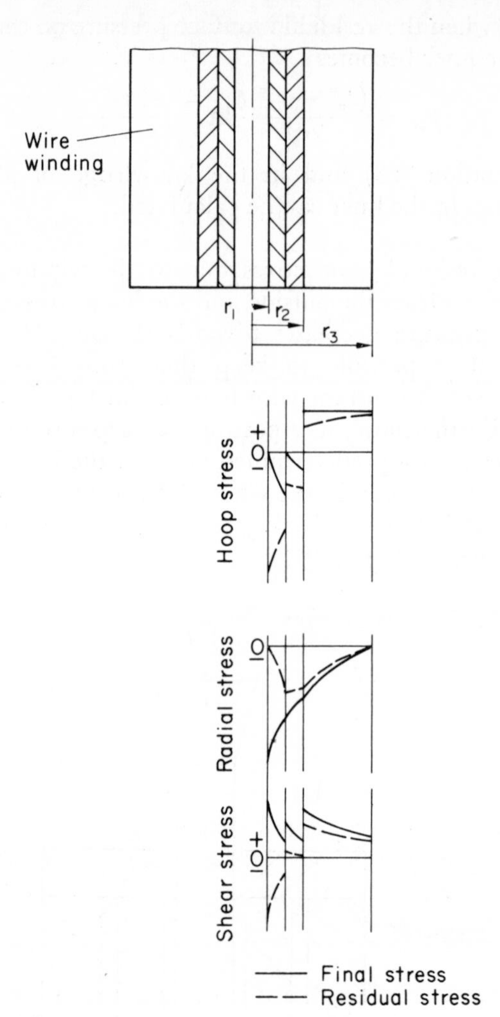

Fig. 29. Wire wound container. (*After Lengyel*, et al., *Ref. 30.*)

To satisfy equation (52) it is necessary to vary the winding tension with the radius, and this requires programmed winding apparatus. It also applies if the hoop stress is limited in the liner, when a material of low ductility, e.g. tungsten carbide is used.

It is much easier to carry out winding at constant wire

tension t, when the residual interface pressure on the outside of the liner becomes

$$p_{2r} = \frac{(r_2^2 - r_1^2)t}{2r_2^2} \ln \frac{r_3^2 - r_1^2}{r_2^2 - r_1^2} \tag{53}$$

From equation (53) and in the knowledge of p_1, the final stresses in the liner can be calculated.

Since the residual hoop stress due to the winding tension decreases from the outside and the hoop stress due to the bore pressure decreases towards the outside in the winding, it is possible to keep their sum reasonably constant even if constant wire tension during winding is applied. Furthermore, it is possible to keep any function of the stresses at a predetermined value at the bore of the liner and at two radii in the winding by a suitable choice of both wire tension t during winding and the outside radius of the winding r_3.[73]

4.1.3.3 *Static Fluid Interface Pressure*

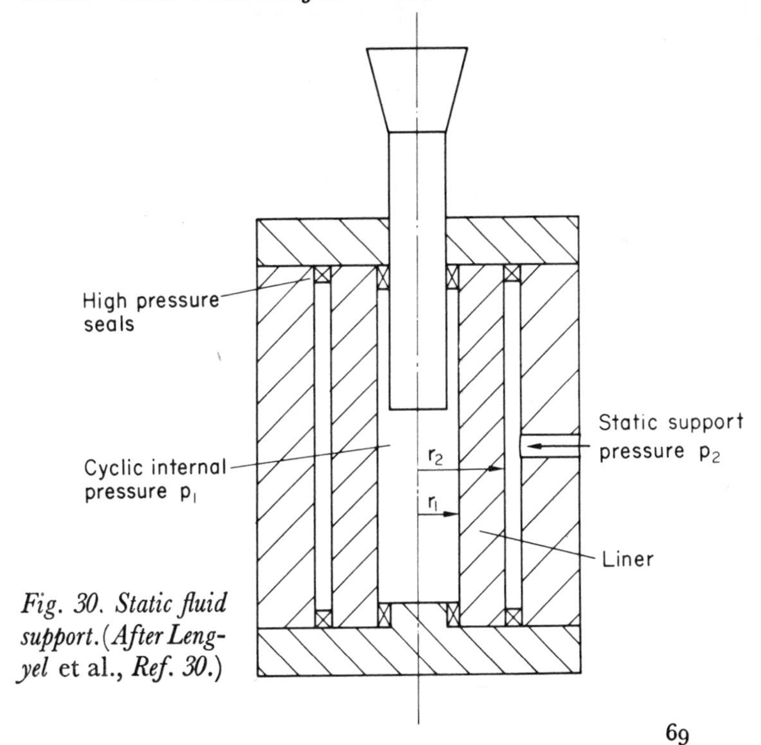

Fig. 30. Static fluid support. (*After Lengyel* et al., *Ref. 30.*)

A further possible alternative design is when the liner is supported by a fluid interlayer at constant pressure (Fig. 30). One advantage is that the liner can be easily replaced in case of failure and that the problems associated with the manufacture of shrink fit or wire wound pressure vessels are absent. If the liner is made of a material of low ductility, the required condition is once more that no tensile hoop stresses must be set up in it under maximum pressure. This gives for the innermost layer for $\sigma_\theta = 0$ in the bore

$$p_2 = \frac{1 + K^2}{2K^2} p_{1\max} = \text{constant} \tag{54}$$

where $$K = \frac{r_2}{r_1}$$

If the pressure fluctuates between zero and a maximum $p_{1\,\max}$ then, for open ends, the stresses become in the bore for zero bore pressure

$$\left.\begin{aligned} \sigma_\theta &= -\frac{K^2 + 1}{K^2 - 1} p_{1\,\max}; \quad \sigma_r = 0; \quad \sigma_z = 0 \\ \tau_{r\theta} &= \frac{K^2 + 1}{2(K^2 - 1)} p_{1\,\max}; \quad \tau_{rz} = 0; \\ \tau_{\theta z} &= \frac{K^2 + 1}{2(K^2 - 1)} p_{1\,\max} \end{aligned}\right\} \tag{55}$$

When $p_{1\,\max}$ is acting the stresses are

$$\left.\begin{aligned} \sigma_\theta &= 0; \quad \sigma_r = -p_{1\,\max}; \quad \sigma_z = 0 \\ \tau_{r\theta} &= \tau_{rz} = \frac{p_{1\,\max}}{2}; \quad \tau_{\theta z} = 0 \end{aligned}\right\} \tag{56}$$

The variation of the hoop stress and the shear stress in the $(r\theta)$ plane, in terms of the ratio $\dfrac{\text{support pressure}}{\text{bore pressure}}$, is shown in Fig. 31.[48] It is clear that, if the pressure in the bore fluctuates between zero and a maximum, with increasing support pressure the range of stresses remains unaltered but the maximum tensile hoop stress is reduced and becomes zero when the condition given by equation (54) is reached. By a suitable choice of p_2 the mean shear stress can be kept zero, an important consideration in design for fatigue.

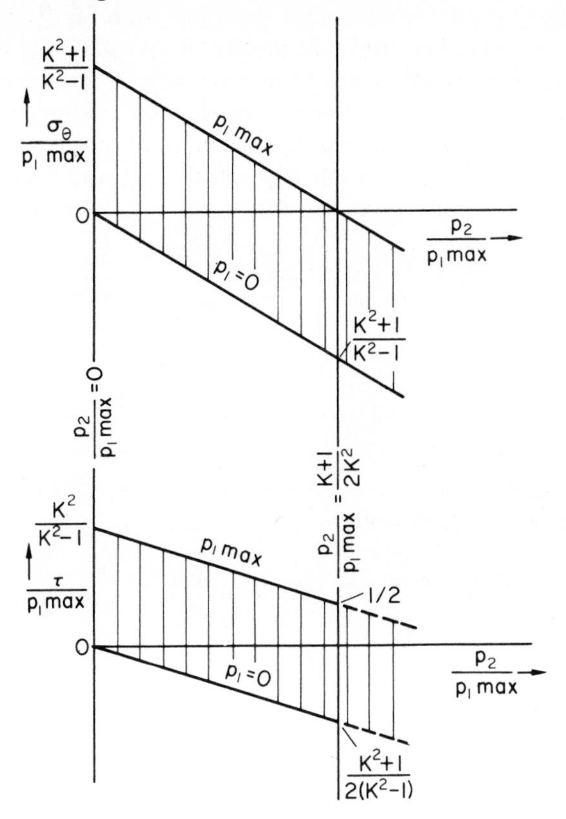

Fig. 31. Stresses in a liner with static fluid support. (*After Harvey* et al., *Ref. 48.*)

4.1.4 *Dynamic Support by Taper Fits*

Bridgman[74] suggested that the liner can be supported on its tapered outside diameter by a cylinder having a matching tapered bore, as illustrated in Fig. 32. The supporting interface pressure p_2 is then built up in proportion to the bore pressure p_1.

The method of optimisation is similar to that discussed for compound shrink or taper fit containers. However, in the calculations two specific points must be taken into account.

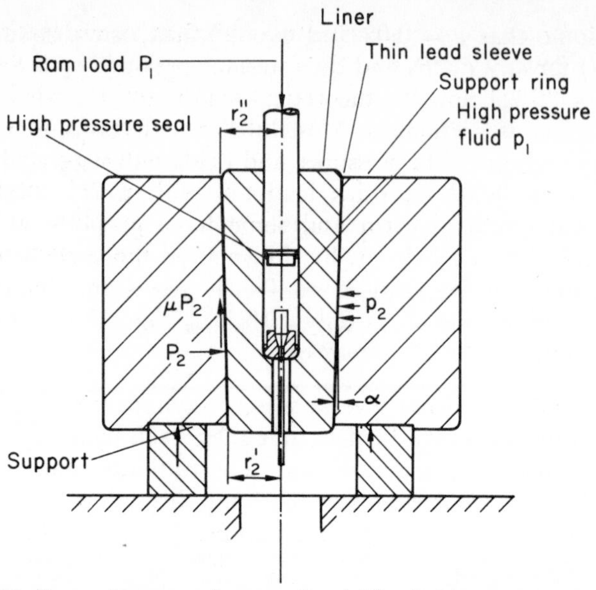

Fig. 32. Dynamic support by taper fits. (After Bridgman, Ref. 74.)

Because load P_1 forces the liner into the outer ring, the support over part of the liner is lost and ultimately the liner could be forced through the bore of the support ring. The relative axial displacement can be calculated from the hoop strains at the interface, from the difference between the elastic expansion of the outer ring bore under pressure p_2 and the expansion of the liner outside diameter under the combined effect of p_1 and p_2.

The effect of the interface friction on p_2 could be significant. By the application of P_1, on loading, if the normal force on the interface is P_2.

$$P_1 = P_2 \sin \alpha + \mu P_2 \cos \alpha \tag{57}$$

where μ is the coefficient of friction.

On unloading

$$P_1' = P_2 \sin \alpha - \mu P_2 \cos \alpha \tag{58}$$

and, by measuring P_1 and P_1' the coefficient of friction can be obtained

$$\mu = \frac{P_1 - P_1'}{P_1 + P_1'} \frac{\sin \alpha}{\cos \alpha} \tag{59}$$

Assume that $\mu = 0{\cdot}02$ and $\alpha = 2°$ then, from equation (57) for any P_1, P_2 and the interface pressure p_2 is found to be 36 % below the theoretical maximum, i.e. when the interface is frictionless. Most lubricants freeze under the very high interface pressures, and Bridgman suggested the use of a 0·002 in. thick lead foil with a 2:1 mixture of water and glycerin and some flake graphite at the interface as a lubricant. By this method the coefficient of friction can be reduced to 0·004, when the interface pressure for $\alpha = 2°$ is only 10 % less than that without friction.

It is possible to use several support cylinders to increase the pressure range further, but then each cylinder must be loaded by a separate ram. The ultimate limit is the possible axial extrusion of the liner through its support. With this arrangement Bridgman reached pressures up to 60 kbar.

4.1.5 *Dynamic Fluid Interface Pressure*

It was also Bridgman's suggestion[75] to immerse a smaller vessel in fluid inside a larger one, then increase the bore pressure and support pressure simultaneously to reach, at their peak, a predetermined ratio (Fig. 33). It is also possible to build the submerged vessel by compounding, when the maximum pressure that can be generated is no longer limited by the strength of the vessel, but by the strength of the punch material. Bridgman thought that, with such arrangement, pressures up to 100 kbar could be reached.

An application of this principle is the floating liner design, shown in Fig. 34.[36] The supporting fluid pressure p_2 is built up by allowing the liner to move axially under the effect of bore pressure p_1. In addition to the advantages of the static fluid support, a further advantage of this design is that the amplitude and maximum values of the stresses can be reduced when the bore pressure fluctuates.

When the bore pressure $p_1 = 0$, then also $p_2 = 0$ and all the stresses are zero:

$$\sigma_\theta = \sigma_r = \sigma_z = \tau_{r\theta} = \tau_{rz} = \tau_{\theta z} = 0.$$

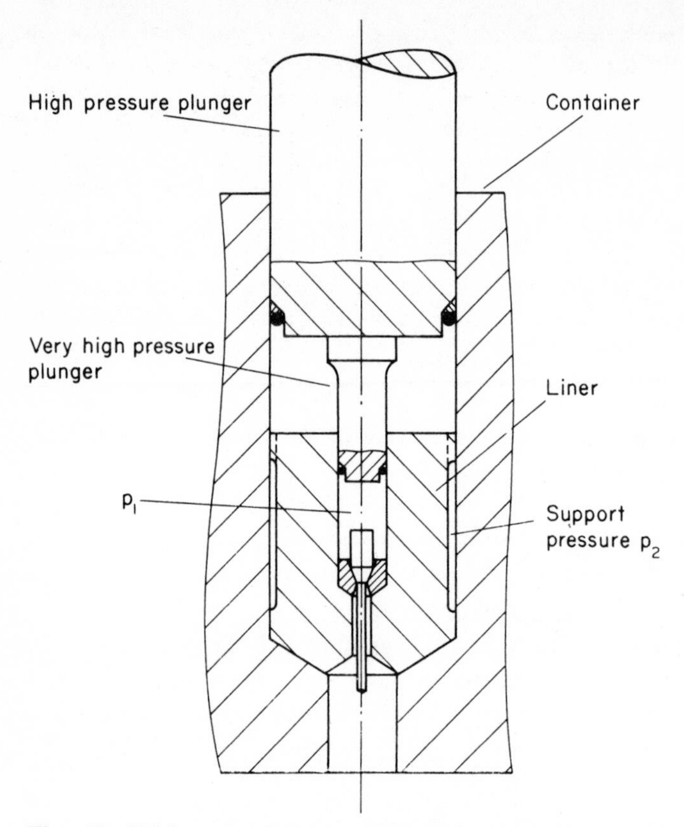

Fig. 33. Bridgman's dynamic fluid support applied to a hydrostatic extrusion container. (After Bridgman, Ref. 75.)

$$\left.\begin{aligned}&\text{When } p_1 > 0 \text{ and}\\ &\qquad \frac{p_2}{p_1} = \frac{1+K^2}{2K^2} = \text{constant}\\ &\text{then, at the bore}\\ &\qquad \sigma_\theta = \sigma_z = 0, \quad \sigma_r = -p_1\\ &\qquad \tau_{r\theta} = \tau_{rz} = \frac{p_1}{2}; \quad \tau_{\theta z} = 0\end{aligned}\right\} \qquad (60)$$

The variation of the hoop stress and shear stress in the $(r\theta)$ plane is shown in Fig. 35.[48] The hoop stress becomes zero at all values of the bore pressure when the conditions

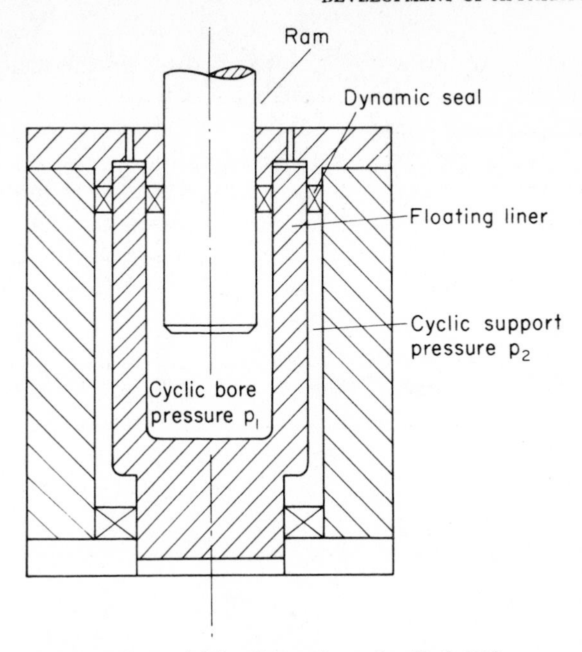

Fig. 34. Floating liner. (*After Lengyel* et al., *Ref. 36.*)

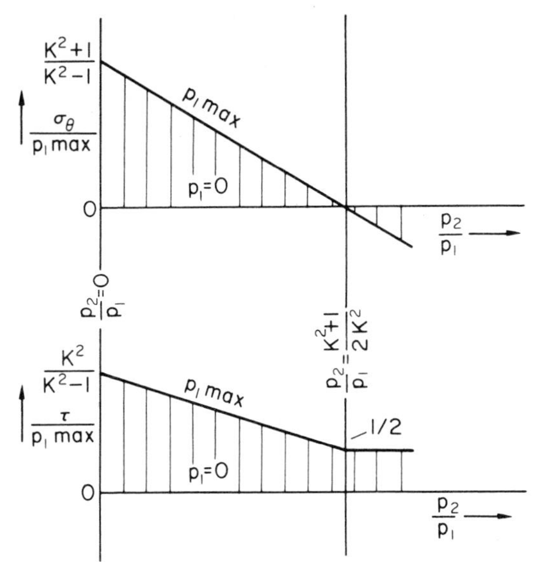

Fig. 35. Stresses in a floating liner. (*After Harvey* et al., *Ref. 48.*)

given by equation (60) are satisfied. Then the maximum shear stress range is reduced to less than half of that for the monobloc vessel which, as will be shown in the next section, is an important consideration in the design of containers for cyclic pressures. The stress conditions are similar when the liner is supported on its tapered outside diameter by another cylinder, the design discussed in the previous section.

4.1.6 *Fatigue Considerations*

The need to consider fatigue in the design of hydrostatic extrusion containers has been mentioned earlier. Considerations and experimental evidence, which could form the basis of such design, will now be discussed briefly.

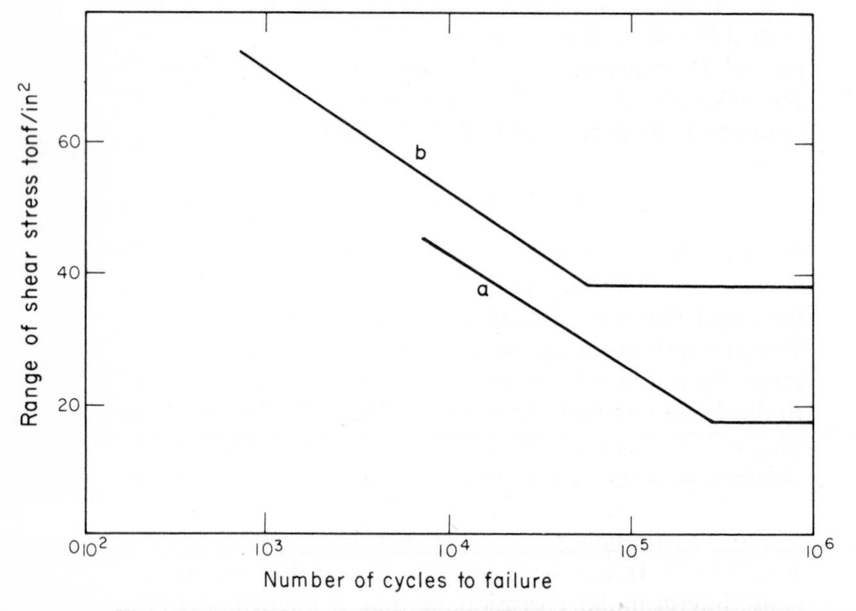

Fig. 36. Fatigue strength of thick-walled cylinders under pressure. a. *Cyclic internal pressure.* b. *Cyclic internal and static external pressure. EN25 steel.*

The fatigue strength of monobloc thick cylinders has been established by subjecting them to repeated internal pressures of up to 3 kbar.[76–78, 48] The results show (Fig. 36) that the range of shear stress at the bore determines failure but, at the fatigue limit, this range is only half the fatigue strength of solid torsion specimens. Furthermore, this ratio of about two varies with different materials and it appears that the fatigue strength of thick cylinders is quite unrelated to any other mechanical property, including the fatigue properties obtained in the usual manner, e.g. in push-pull, bending or torsional fatigue tests. One seemingly plausible explanation was that this relatively low strength is caused by the presence of the triaxial tensile stress, which is superimposed on a pure shear in closed-end thick cylinders under internal pressure; this had to be discarded immediately, however, because no effect of K on the fatigue strength has been found, despite a variation of the hydrostatic tensile stress with different K ratios (equations 19 to 21). It has been proved by experiments under various conditions[79] that the reduction in strength is unrelated to the presence of hydrostatic tension; variation in the axial stress

$$(\sigma_z = \sigma_\theta, \tfrac{2}{3}\sigma_\theta, \tfrac{1}{3}\sigma_\theta, 0, \sigma_r)$$

has no effect on fatigue life, if the other two principal stresses are kept substantially constant. Investigations indicated that the effect of fluid is a contributory factor. The strength of the cylinders increases if the bore is protected by a thin rubber sleeve, when the fluid is no longer in direct contact with the cylinder wall. Whether this is a physical or chemical effect, or both, is not clear, but the deleterious effect of the hydraulic oil has been shown to exist also in torsional and push-pull fatigue tests, whether the oil surrounding the specimen is pressurised or not.[77, 80, 81] It has been suggested that the oil might cause intergranular corrosion, or that it might penetrate surface imperfections and raise the stresses above the nominal level, but no direct proof of either effect has yet been found.

The fatigue strength in the mortal region could be of particular importance in container design, so it is worth mentioning that similar correlation between the maximum shear stress and the pressure cycles to failure has been found beyond the elastic limit, if the maximum shear stress is calculated from elastic considerations.[82]

Available information indicates that a maraging steel cylinder of 103 tonf/in^2 proof stress is not significantly stronger in fatigue than a cylinder of EN25 steel of half that proof stress. For both steels the 10^5 endurance limit was found at 28 tonf/in^2. For this reason, the fatigue strength of monobloc cylinders cannot be increased significantly by using materials of very high tensile strength. Furthermore, since the endurance limit is little affected by K for non-autofrettaged cylinders, no substantial increase can be achieved beyond $K = 4$. Thus the maximum cyclic bore pressure that a non-autofrettaged monobloc cylinder can support for 10^5 cycles is limited to about 6 kbar (from equation 22), even if made from the strongest materials on which data are at present available.

Cylinders with $K = 1{\cdot}6$ and 2 (with the bores exposed to the fluid) showed an increase of about 10% in fatigue strength when autofrettaged to the mean radius.[78] When autofrettaged cylinders of $K = 2$ were fully over-strained, the increase in pressure was about 70% at 10^5 pressure cycles, which represents the maximum benefit that can be gained by autofrettage owing to reverse yield with full overstrain at higher K ratios. It can thus be concluded that monobloc cylinders, autofrettaged or otherwise, can be excluded for many industrial applications in hydrostatic extrusion, if a life of 10^5 pressure cycles or more is required.

Fig. 28 illustrates a typical stress distribution in a five-component shrink fit compound container. Apart from the outermost cylinder which can be treated as a monobloc vessel under cyclic internal pressure, there are two loading modes; in the innermost cylinder the pressure cycles between 0 and a maximum, while the outer pressure fluctuates between two relatively close values, neither of them zero. The intermediate cylinders are subjected to a relatively low range of pressure cycles both internally and externally, with mean pressures which are significant relative to the pressure range.

On the basis of experimental evidence it seems likely that the maximum shear stress range in the bore is the primary factor in causing fatigue failure of the components, but there are secondary factors also. It is well known that a reduced mean shear stress and residual compressive stresses increase fatigue life. The increased fatigue strength of autofrettaged cylinders illustrates that this is also valid for thick cylinders. Further proof of these secondary effects is furnished by the result of fatigue tests on two-component compound vessels[85]: for zero mean stress and a life of 10^5 pressure cycles, the range of maximum bore shear stress could be increased by about 40 %.

The conclusion can then be drawn that, to improve the fatigue characteristics of a monobloc thick cylinder, or of the component cylinders of a compound container, the range of shear stress, the mean shear stress and the maximum tensile stress should be reduced. From available experimental evidence, it is not clear which of the latter two stress functions is the determining secondary factor.

A comparison of Figs. 23 and 28 shows that the maximum value of the tensile hoop stress and mean shear stress are reduced in an open-ended compound container relative to that in a monobloc vessel, and both can be reduced to zero in the bore of the two inner components. Similar conditions can be achieved in the liner of a wire-wound vessel or in the liners of compound containers with static or cyclic interface pressure by a suitable selection of the support pressure, as Figs. 31 and 35 indicate. In addition to the possibility of eliminating the tensile hoop stress and the mean shear stress, the maximum range of shear stress can be reduced in the liner by the application of a dynamic interfacial pressure (Fig. 35).

The final conclusion can then be drawn that it is possible to design compound containers which are significantly superior to monobloc vessels in fatigue, whether the latter are autofrettaged or not. The main difficulty is the lack of sufficient data on the fatigue behaviour of thick cylinders under combined internal and external pressures. This applies particularly to the liner which, for very high pressures, must be made of materials of low ductility such as tool steel or tungsten carbide and for these materials fatigue data for the required stress conditions are completely absent. Until such data become available, design studies on compound containers for cyclic pressures must be based at least partly on assumptions.[30, 47, 86]

4.2 EXTRUSION DIE AND PRESSURISING RAM

To support large bore pressures, compound dies are often used in conventional extrusion; they are bulky and expensive. In hydrostatic extrusion, the fluid pressure supports the die (Fig. 37*a*), which can be made thin and easily replaceable. Furthermore, the conical portion subjected to wear can be made from a very hard and wear-resistant material, the die support being made from a tougher steel (Fig. 37*b*).

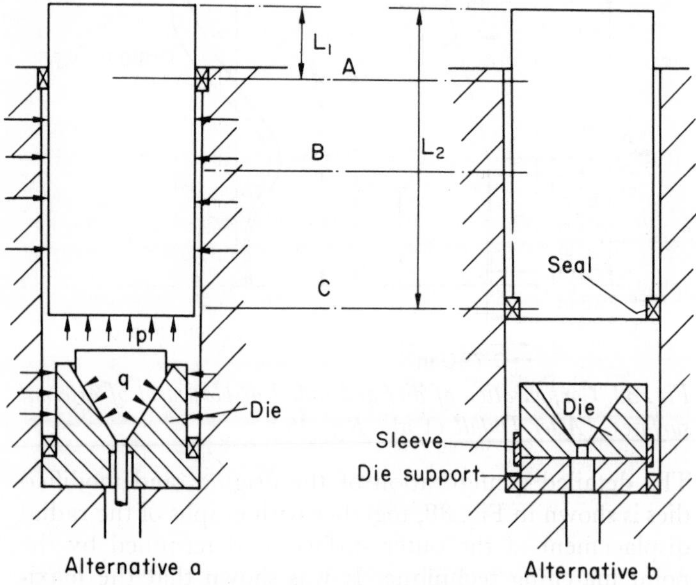

Fig. 37. Extrusion die and plunger arrangements.

The elastic stress distribution in a hydrostatic extrusion die was calculated using an iterative method named "the point matching technique".[46] A typical die shape was considered and a pressure distribution assumed in the form

$$q = \frac{p_E}{\ln R}\left[1 + \ln \frac{A}{A_2}\right]$$

where q = normal pressure on the die
p_E = experimentally-measured extrusion pressure
R = extrusion ratio
A = cross-sectional area of the billet at any given position within the die
A_2 = cross-sectional area of billet at exit.

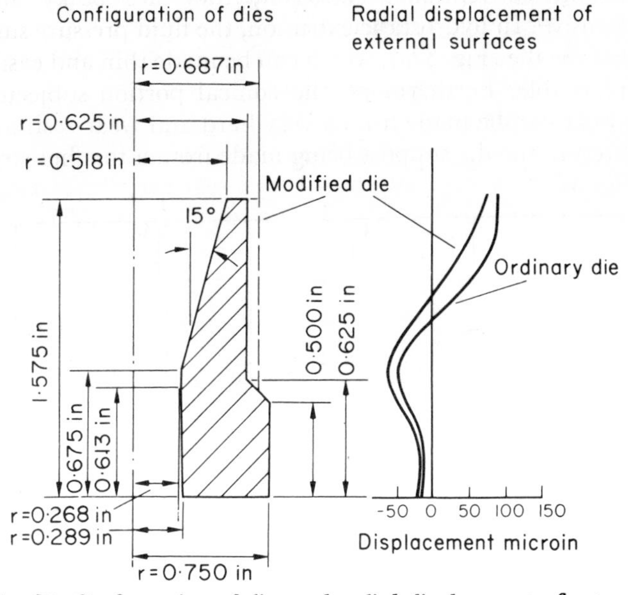

Fig. 38. Configuration of dies and radial displacement of external surfaces. (After Duffill et al., *Ref. 46.)*

The detailed configuration of the original and modified dies is shown in Fig. 38, together with graphs of the radial displacement of the outer surface as determined by the point matching technique. It was shown that the maximum tensile stresses in the original die shape occur as hoop stresses on the conical face and axial stresses along the die land. All other stresses are predominantly compressive. The tensile hoop stresses could be significantly reduced by modification to the die shape, in fact they could be converted on the upper outer face into compressive stresses.

The plunger can be designed either to carry a moving seal as indicated in Fig. 37*b*, or the seal can be stationary, supported by the container (Fig. 37*a*) or by a separate end piece. Assume that pressurisation of the fluid begins when the plunger reaches position A, completed at B and, as it proceeds to C, extrusion takes place at a constant pressure p. If the seal is carried by the plunger, the total length L_2 is unsupported at the end of stroke. While this design is simple, for larger pressure and long plungers the arrangement shown in Fig. 37*a* is preferable, because the unsupported plunger length reduces to L_1; thus, the danger of buckling decreases.

The pressure discontinuity at the seal introduces stress discontinuities in the container wall which could be significant. This effect is illustrated in Fig. 39 for a pressure discontinuity and container of given proportions.[87] The axial tensile stress could be particularly detrimental, since it could lead to early fatigue failure. Such failures have in fact been observed in the form of circumferential fractures in extrusion containers with hard liners. While this effect in alternative (*a*) is restricted to the container end, the stress discontinuity in alternative (*b*) travels with the seal and introduces poor fatigue conditions along the wall between A and C.

A further consideration in plunger seal design is that, between positions A and C, in alternative (*b*) the container wall is subjected to twice the number of pressure cycles than in alternative (*a*); thus, for fatigue, the design illustrated in Fig. 37*a* seems preferable.

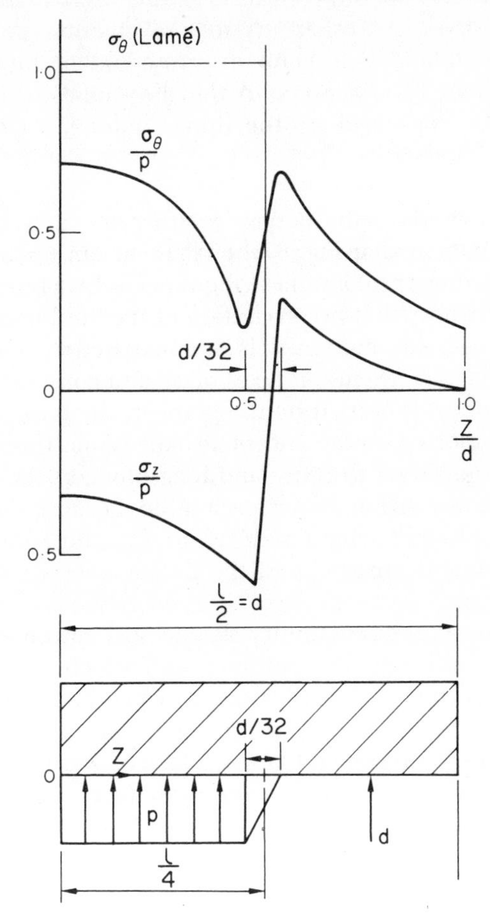

Length of container $l = 2 \times$ bore diameter

$K = 6{\cdot}25 \quad \nu = 0{\cdot}3$

Fig. 39. Effect of pressure discontinuity on the bore stresses of an extrusion container. (*After Kudo* et al., *Ref. 87.*)

4.3 SEALS AND CLAMPS

In experimental work on hydrostatic extrusion, and in the development of the process for industrial applications, a number of sealing problems face the designer. Satisfactory solutions are available which give a reasonable seal life for up to 30 kbar pressures in experimental work when only a small number of pressure applications is required; these designs cannot be used without further modification, however, if the number of pressure cycles is large, such as for the container of a production machine, when the seal life could ideally extend over 10^5 or more pressure cycles.

Seals for the production machine can be divided broadly into two main groups, (1) those which seal between elastic components of the equipment and (2) those which seal around the billet material, where the billet is introduced into the container in semi-continuous hydrostatic extrusion. In the first type of application, various designs have successfully withstood up to 8 kbar pressures for a large number of pressure cycles (10^4 or over) and similar seal life appears to be within reach for higher pressures. However, no test results have been published so far to prove the satisfactory functioning of the devices proposed to seal and clamp around the billet material, a vital requirement for a very important component of the semi-continuous hydrostatic extrusion production machine.

In hydrostatic extrusion, or in experimental work connected with the development of hydrostatic extrusion for industrial applications, fluid seals for different functional requirements must be provided in various parts of the equipment (Fig. 7 and Fig. 11):

(*a*) Dynamic seals between the ram and container.
(*b*) Static seals between the die and container.
(*c*) Billet seals in semi-continuous hydrostatic extrusion.
(*d*) Sealing between billet and die.

4.3.1 *Dynamic Seals between Ram and Container*
Most dynamic seals could be used either as stationary or moving seals, as discussed in section 4.2. Here, only one alternative will be illustrated.

The unsupported area seal has been developed by Bridgman[88] and used by many research workers, both as dynamic and static seals. In the seal illustrated in Fig. 40

the pressure is larger than the fluid pressure by the ratio of areas $A_1 : A_2$.[89] No fluid can leak past the seal if the pressure in the seal material is sufficiently high, but then there is the danger that a "dry seal" is produced with high frictional forces and possible scoring of the container wall. This is the reason for providing a reservoir of lubricant in the design illustrated in Fig. 40. A further possible source of trouble is the stem, which can fracture under the lateral pressure exerted on it by the seal ("pinching-off effect").

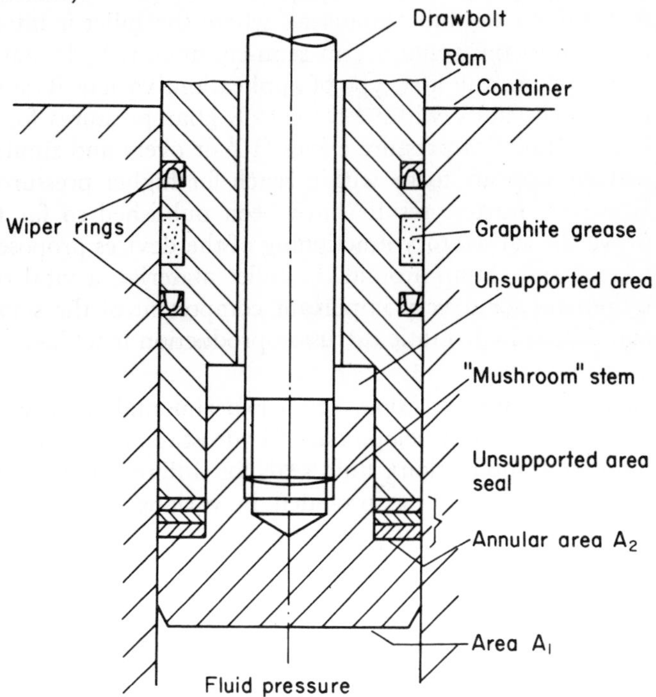

Fig. 40. Unsupported area seal. (After Mikhaev, Ref. 89.)

The simplicity and cheapness of the O-ring seal made it popular with research workers. This seal also gives a reasonably good service for a limited number of cycles in both dynamic and static applications if supported by anti-extrusion rings. The O-ring seal with an anti-extrusion mitre ring, illustrated in Fig. 41, is being used widely for pressures up to 20 kbar. One limitation of this method is the well-known disadvantage of O-ring seals, that they roll and twist and fail prematurely in dynamic applications.

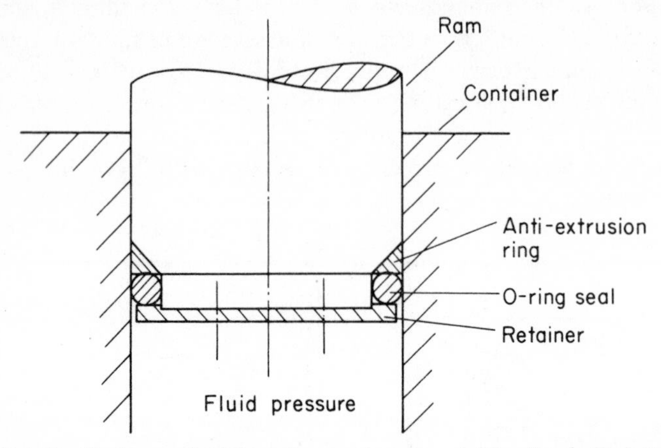

Fig. 41. O-ring seal with anti-extrusion ring. (*After Pugh, Ref. 5.*)

No such problems exist with the V-ring or Chevron seals, illustrated in Fig. 42. These are made of leather or synthetic rubber and, when assembled, the lips are pre-loaded to ensure initial sealing. Male and female support rings are used at the two ends of a stack of V-rings, the latter serving as anti-extrusion rings.

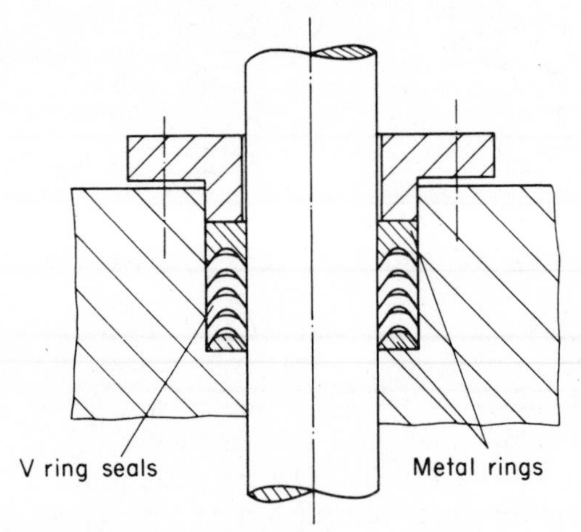

Fig. 42. V-ring seal arrangement.

Another possible shape, which eliminates some of the disadvantages of the O-ring while retaining its simplicity, is the D-ring illustrated in Fig. 43. In all these methods there is a further hazard in that, at high pressures, the radial clearance between the ram and container becomes large and the mitre ring extrudes into the gap, with the result of high frictional forces and possible surface damage to the container or plunger.

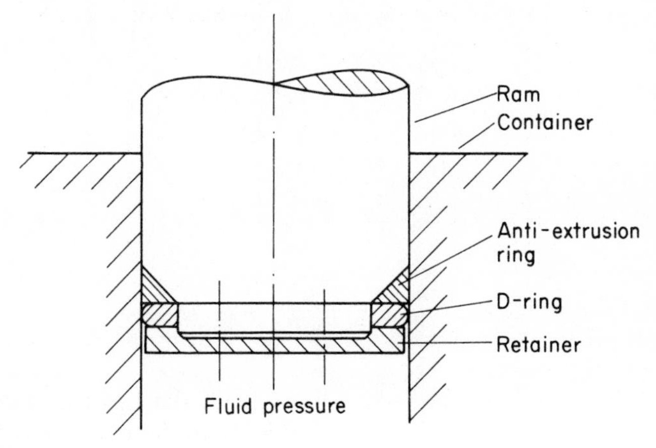

Fig. 43. D-ring seal with anti-extrusion ring.

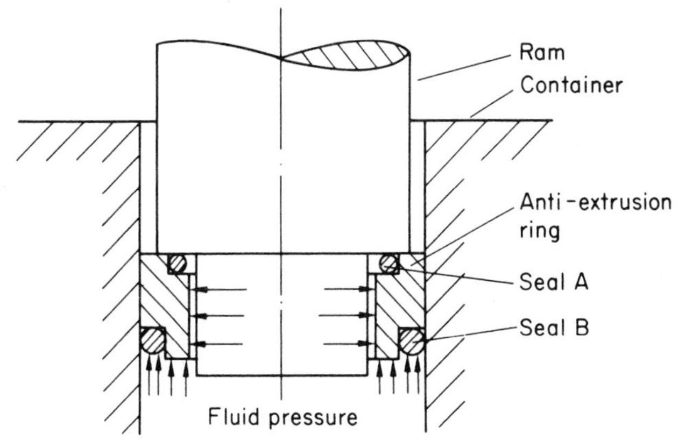

Fig. 44. Expanding anti-extrusion ring. (After Zeitlin et al., *Ref. 90.)*

One method which allows for the radial movement of the container wall is to design an anti-extrusion ring which expands and contracts with it,[90] such as that illustrated in Fig. 44. The pressure on the end-face of the ring forces it against the plunger, preventing seal A from extruding radially, while the pressure in the bore of the ring forces it against the container wall; thus, an effective anti-extrusion ring is produced which prevents seal B from extruding in the axial direction. A more sophisticated alternative of the same principle is shown in Fig. 45.[91]

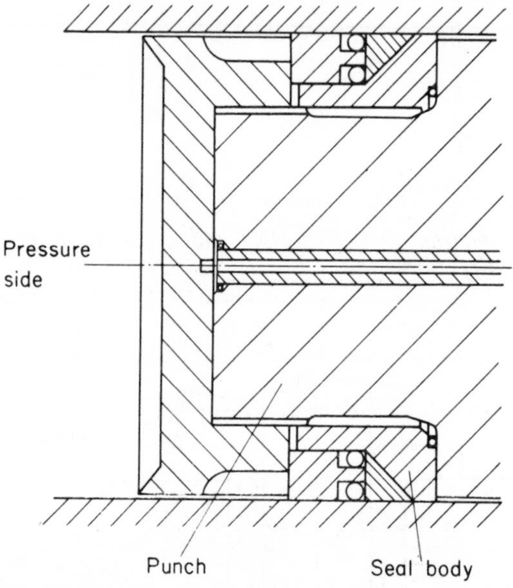

Fig. 45. Punch seal for 1600/80 Fielding Hydrostat. (After Green, Ref. 91.)

Another method relies on the comparative ease with which static seals can work well in conditions where dynamic seals would present a major problem.[92] (Fig. 46).

All elastic expansion of the container bore is taken up by static mitre ring A, while the clearance at B remains substantially unaltered during the pressure cycle.

The radial clearance between a moving ram and the

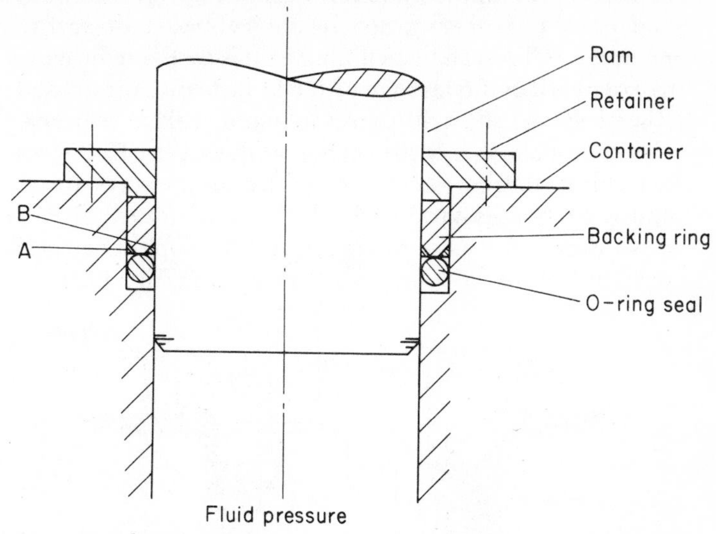

Fig. 46. O-ring seal with two anti-extrusion rings. (After Paterson, Ref. 92.)

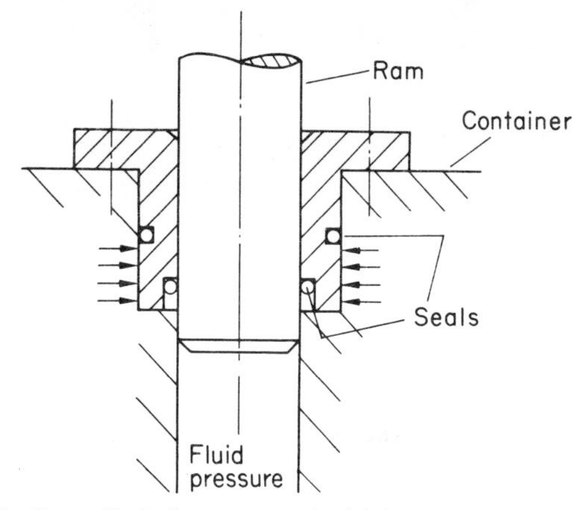

Fig. 47. Controlled clearance seal. (After Daniels, Ref. 93.)

adjoining part is controlled by applying outside pressure to the sleeve in the design illustrated in Fig. 47, creating more advantageous conditions for the satisfactory functioning of the dynamic seal.[93] Also, the controlled clearance method is used in the lip seal shown in Fig. 48, where the fluid pressure is transmitted by the rubber static seal to the sleeve.[76] The radial clearance in this case is reduced to an extent when the leakage of the fluid between ram and sleeve becomes so small that no separate seal is required. This type of seal has performed well at very high ram speeds for a large number of cycles at pressures up to approximately 5 kbar.

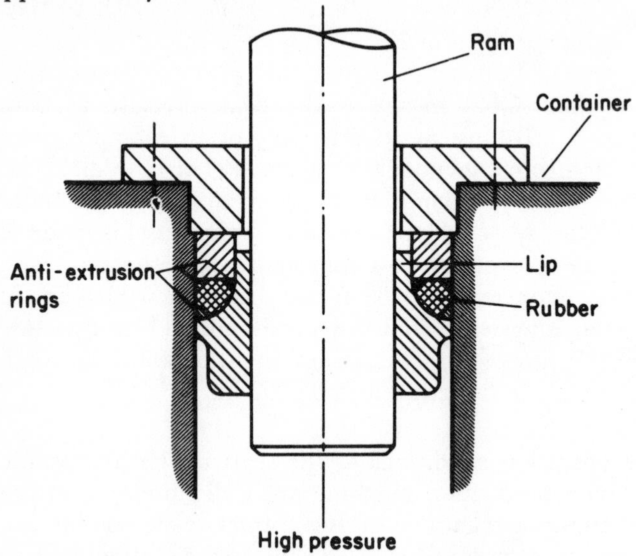

Fig. 48. Lip seal. (*After Morrison* et al., *Ref. 76.*)

In a further method, the clearance at the dynamic seal is controlled by reducing the radial elastic dilatation of the container bore.[36] Generally, the radial elastic expansion of a pressure vessel bore is

$$u = \frac{r}{E}[\sigma_\theta - \nu(\sigma_r + \sigma_z)] \tag{61}$$

where r is the bore radius, σ_θ, σ_r and σ_z are the hoop, radial and axial stresses in the bore, E is Young's modulus and ν is Poisson's ratio. This expression indicates possible methods of reducing the undesirable radial expansion of the vessel. Either a material of large Young's modulus can be used for the liner, such as tungsten carbide, or the hoop stress in the bore can be reduced, or both.

The bore hoop stress at all values of the bore pressure becomes zero when dynamic interface pressure is used (e.g. Fig. 34) and its ratio to the bore pressure is constant at the value given by equation (60). Then, for an open-ended container with zero axial stress in the wall, the radial expansion from equation (61) is reduced to

$$u = \frac{r_1}{E}\nu(p_1)_{max} \quad (62)$$

and is independent of K.

In equation (62) $(p_1)_{max}$ is the peak pressure at bore radius r_1. To illustrate this by way of an example given in reference 69, a monobloc steel vessel of $r_1 = 2{\cdot}125$ in. and $K = 5{\cdot}65$ expands in the bore by 0·0035 in. under 35,000 lbf/in² (2·4 kbar) pressure. If the vessel is made of the same size but with a tungsten carbide liner of 3 in. outside diameter, the expansion becomes 0·0018 in. If the same tungsten carbide liner is supported by a dynamic fluid pressure p_2 which satisfies equation (60), the bore expansion can be reduced to 0·0002 in.

The operation conditions of the seals in the hydrostatic extrusion production machine are well simulated in the low endurance fatigue tests of thick-walled cylinders. Here, the cyclic pressures are the highest attempted so far in prolonged testing; up to 6 kbar has been reported in one work[82] and over 8 kbar is often used in another.[48] Besides testing the cylinders, these fatigue tests are probably the best methods for development and testing of seals under dynamic conditions at high pressures. The results indicate that unit seals with anti-extrusion rings perform well, such as the SCN ring[82] illustrated in Fig. 49 and the Hallprene seal[48] shown in Fig. 50.

The Hallprene seal is a square-based U-ring of synthetic rubber impregnated fabric bonded to a soft rubber section, which acts as a filler and pretensioner of the lips. The soft rubber also transmits pressure to the fabric backing which then fills the gap and acts as an anti-extrusion ring. Phosphor bronze mitre rings have been used to prevent the extrusion of the fabric at these high pressures. The probable reason for the satisfactory functioning of this arrangement is that, at the moving plunger, the radial gap is reasonably constant, while at the bore of the specimen—where large elastic dilatations occur—there is no relative movement between the parts adjoining the seal, a condition very similar to that illustrated in Fig. 46.

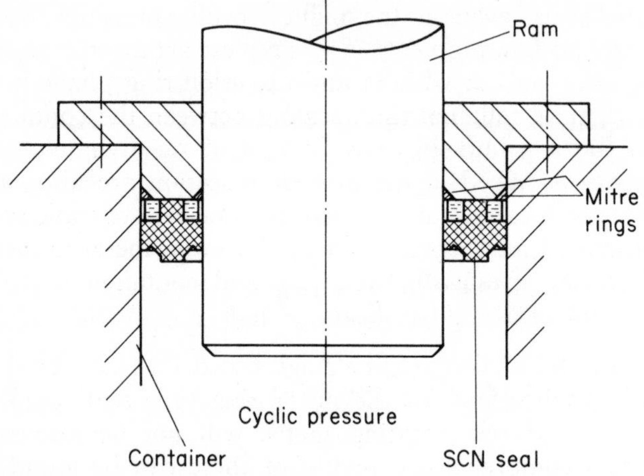

Fig. 49 S.C.N. seal with phosphor bronze mitre rings. (*After Austin* et al., *Ref. 82.*)

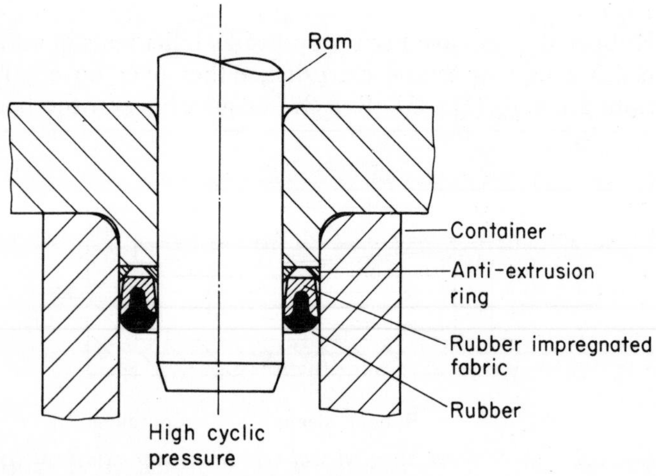

Fig. 50. Hallprene seal with mitre rings.

The SCN ring is another pressure-energised seal. When fitted, the lips are lightly compressed to provide initial sealing. Pressure on the working face is transmitted through the rubber ring to the fabric, which expands and prevents extrusion of the rubber. In this application (Fig. 49) the fabric is further backed up by metal mitre rings.

4.3.2 *Static Seals between Die and Container*

Static seals, even at the highest cyclic pressures, seem to present few problems. The simplest arrangements, O-ring seals with or without anti-extrusion rings, have been found quite reliable; thus, sealing between the container and die is relatively easy. Several of the dynamic seal designs described in the preceding section are also suitable as static seals, and a separate discussion of static seals is therefore unnecessary. Often the large metal-to-metal interfacial pressure between die and container alone is sufficient to prevent leakage.

Metallic seals such as cone rings and delta rings, used in static applications, or the piston-ring type seals used to seal around reciprocating shafts, will not be discussed here: a comprehensive review of these can be found in reference 94.

4.3.3 *Billet Clamps and Seals in Semi-continuous Hydrostatic Extrusion*

Rubber sleeves have been proposed as billet seals in semi-continuous hydrostatic extrusion, either over an axially slotted clamp (Fig. 51, Ref. 37) or as a liner in the bore

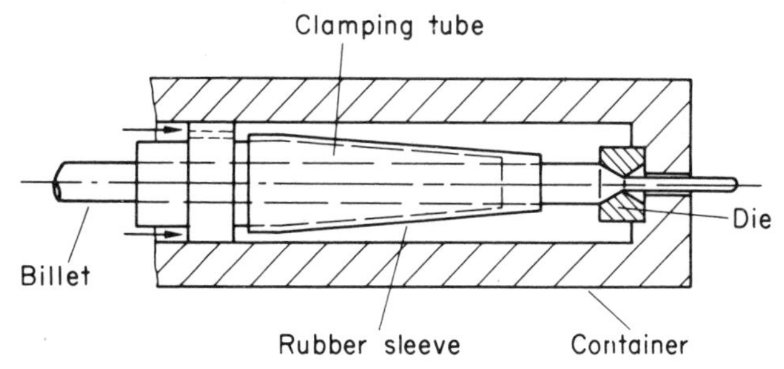

Fig. 51. Rubber sleeve as billet seal over the clamp axially slotted near its leading edge. (After Slater et al., *Ref. 37.)*

of such a clamp.[95] In yet another device (Fig. 52), under pressure the clamp is without gaps or slots and the billet material expands into it rather than the "clamp" contracting on to the billet material.[32]

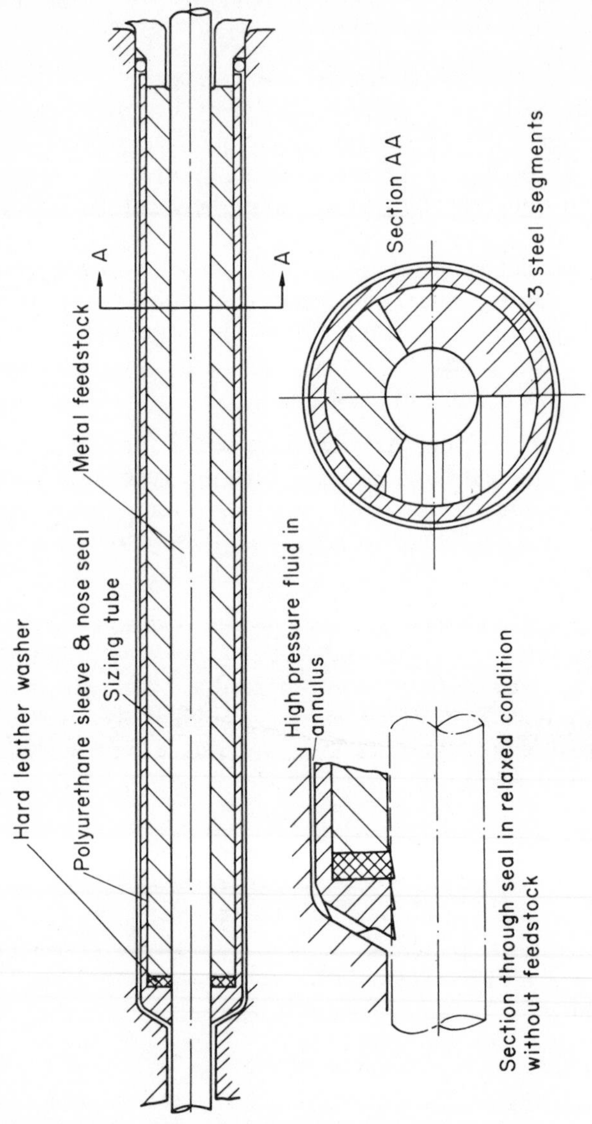

Fig. 52. Sizing tube. (*After Lengyel* et al., *Ref. 32.*)

Earlier experiments show that a simple 4-jaw clamp allows the billet to extrude between the clamp jaws at the front, the extruded flash diminishing towards the back end of the clamp (Fig. 53). The length of the clamp (l_0), necessary to prevent the billet material from being ejected through the entry-end of the container, can be calculated easily by considering the equilibrium of the billet. It is evident that the clamp/billet interface pressure towards the front end approaches the container pressure, and for large extrusion ratios this is much greater than the yield stress of the billet material, while at a distance l_1 from the front end it has a value less than the yield stress of the billet material. Figure 53 indicates that, if clamping marks are to be prevented, length l_1 of the clamp must be a continuous tube ("sizing tube") fully enclosing the billet material, the geometry of the back-end (length $l_0 - l_1$) being unimportant. This separation of functions has led to the concept of the sizing tube.

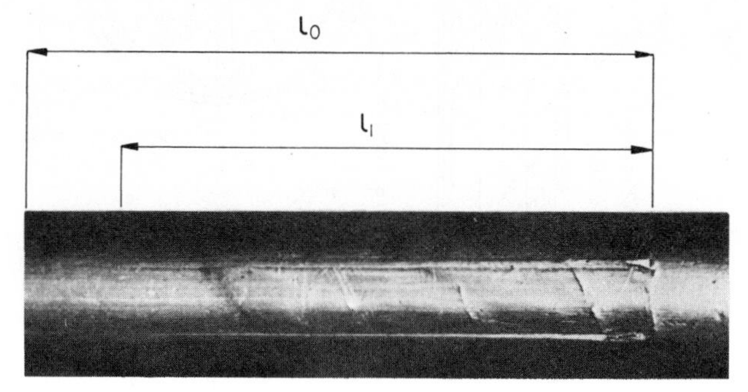

Fig. 53. Clamping marks on aluminium specimen. (After Alexander et al., *Ref. 29.)*

Now the design should aim at the development of devices capable of clamping hot rolled or cast billets with large diametral tolerances. The sizing tube must accommodate all billets within the dimensional limits and the smaller sizes must be upset to fill it, otherwise the sizing tube as a clamp would become ineffective. To achieve this objective, it is envisaged that the billet material is first clamped at the back-end and sealed at the front (Fig. 54), so that the portion within the sizing tube is effectively in compression. As soon as the yield stress of the billet material is reached it begins to fill the tube, and the surface friction along the length of the tube will provide a gradually increasing axial force which counteracts the force acting on the billet cross-sectional area due to the fluid pressure. The interface pressure and axial force are proportional to the container pressure, and all but a small portion of the ejecting force could be carried by a tube of suitable length (l_1). The radial compressive stress at the clamp/billet interface at the rear of the sizing tube remains substantially at a value equal to or less than the yield stress of the billet material; thus, extrusion of the billet between the clamp jaws cannot occur. The sizing tube must be made of several sections which are closed without joint gaps before the container is pressurised and open during the feed stroke.

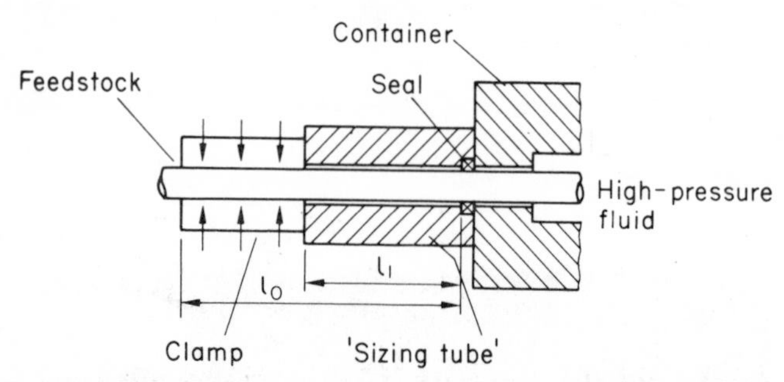

Fig. 54. Sizing tube principle. (*After Lengyel* et al., *Ref. 32.*)

The design being developed in an experimental preproduction machine is illustrated in Fig. 52. The sizing tube consists of a segmented tube sealed by a polyurethane sleeve and held together without gaps by fluid pressure on its outside, the pressure being released to free the bar during the feed cycle. At the high pressure end, sealing is effected by a nose seal backed by a hard leather washer. Initial support for the feed stock against the ejecting axial load is given by a light clamping force exerted by four long clamp jaws to the right of Fig. 52, not shown. The seals must prevent leakage when the container is depressurised and new billet material is being fed into it, so that at low pressure they function as dynamic seals. At high pressure, however, no relative movement of the adjoining components and billet takes place; in the critical condition, therefore, the billet seals function as static seals. The main difficulty associated with their development is that the diameter of the billet material is likely to vary widely and the billet seals must function under such conditions for a large number of pressure cycles.

4.3.4 *Sealing between Billet and Die*

No separate seal is necessary to prevent the escape of fluid between billet and die. The billet nose, which is machined to the die angle is initially forced against the die either by gravity in orthodox hydrostatic extrusion, or by the augmentation ram in billet augmentation, or by pulling the tag in product augmentation. During extrusion, additional force is supplied by the fluid pressure acting over the full cross-sectional area of the billet, while the area at the die exit is unsupported. The resultant interfacial pressure between billet and die prevents the escape of fluid.

4.4 SELECTION OF FLUIDS

Orthodox hydrostatic extrusion is often regarded as a process in which frictional losses are low, since, in contrast to conventional extrusion, a common billet/container interface is no longer present and friction along the billet/die interface is greatly reduced as an abundant supply of lubricant (the pressurised fluid) is available where it is needed most, at the die entry. Traces of fluid have been found on the extruded rods; this has led to the suggestion that, in the steady state, hydrodynamic lubrication conditions are likely to exist, i.e. billet and die are effectively separated by a layer of fluid. At the beginning of extrusion, at low speed, boundary lubrication conditions are present; as the billet speed builds up, friction decreases because a pressurised fluid layer is established at the billet/die interface, with a pressure sufficient to deform the material and to support the extrusion load. The extrusion pressure versus time recordings usually show a definite initial peak followed by a substantial drop in extrusion pressure, indicating the point where boundary friction has been replaced by hydrodynamic lubrication.

Such evidence as exists to prove this mechanism is indirect. No one has yet carried out detailed measurements of the amount of fluid transferred through the die to supply the lubricant layer in full fluid or in mixed lubrication, or of the pressure of the interfacial fluid layer, or established the critical conditions for hydrodynamic conditions, such as billet velocity, viscosity of fluid and extrusion pressure.

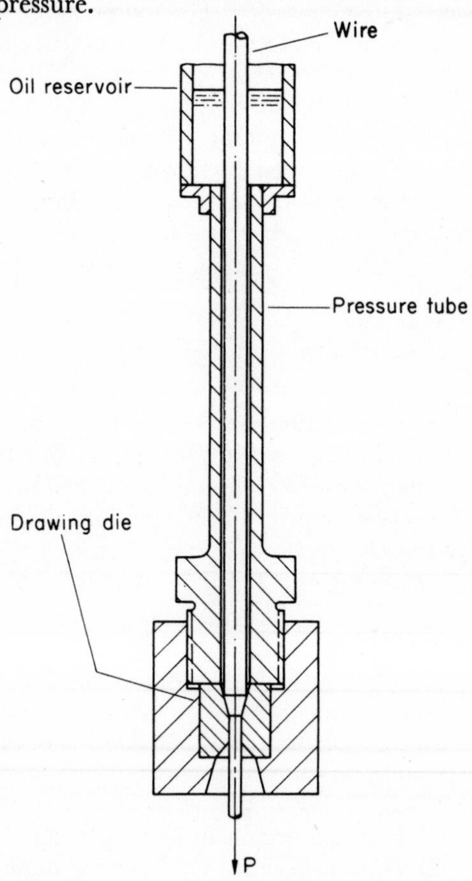

Fig. 55. Wire drawing with pressure tube. (*After Christopherson* et al., *Ref. 96.*)

However, investigations of somewhat similar conditions in wire drawing have been carried out earlier.[96] In this work, lubricating oil to the die was supplied under pressure by passing the wire through a reservoir and a tube, on its way to the die (Fig. 55). Lubricant is drawn into the tube by the wire, causing pressure build-up along the tube and at the wire/die interface. It has been shown that, if the clearance between wire and tube is small and a critical wire speed is reached, sufficient fluid pressure could be produced to deform the wire. At this stage, an increased amount of fluid flows through the die along the wire/die interface, until a minimum friction is reached and complete fluid lubrication is established. On the assumption that the wire is located centrally in the tube and is uniform in diameter, the thickness of the oil film in the die could be calculated.

It has been suggested that, under these conditions, the lubricant layer near the wire surface is being forced out of the die faster than the wire itself, i.e. the lubricant flow in effect assists the motion of the wire (Fig. 56); this is quite unlike the condition in Coulomb friction, when the frictional drag opposes the wire motion and is additional to the drawing force. Furthermore, substantial reduction in die wear has been recorded when pressurised oil lubrication was used instead of the conventional dry soap lubricants. All these findings are likely also to be applicable to orthodox hydrostatic extrusion in the steady state.

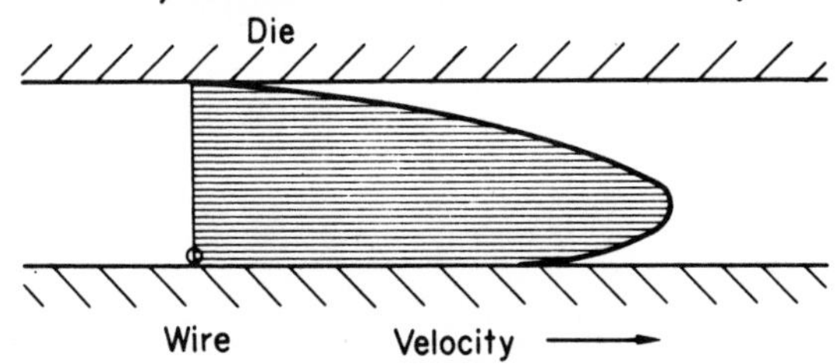

Fig. 56. Lubricant flow in the die. (After Christopherson et al.*, Ref. 96.)*

In deriving the pressure generated in the tube and the frictional drag on the wire, use has been made of the Reynolds lubrication equations. A pressure-viscosity relationship of the exponential form has been assumed

$$z = z_0 e^{\gamma p} \tag{63}$$

where z is the viscosity at pressure p, z_0 is the viscosity at atmospheric pressure and γ is a constant, characteristic of a particular oil. An estimate of the temperature of the fluid layer has been made with the assumptions that (*a*) sufficient time is available for the heat generated by the frictional drag on the wire in the tube to raise the wire temperature uniformly across the cross-section and (*b*) that the lubricant layer in the tube is thin, its temperature thus being only a few degrees above that of the wire. If calculated on the first assumption, the wire temperature can be shown to increase by 1·4°C for each tonf/in^2 (154 bar) pressure. Since the pressure at the die entry did not exceed about 1·5 kbar for soft copper and 3 kbar for mild steel wire, the temperature increase of the oil and its effect on viscosity was small.

In orthodox hydrostatic extrusion, pressures are much higher than in wire drawing, from 10 kbar upwards; therefore, temperature effects on the viscosity of the fluid cannot be neglected. For example, in the extrusion of copper at a ratio of 16, product temperatures of up to 420°C have been measured.[61]

The importance of pressure and temperature effects on viscosity is illustrated by another work in which the rolling of thin sheets has been considered with hydrodynamic lubrication in the roll gap.[97] The viscosity was assumed to vary with pressure p and temperature T according to the relation

$$z = z_0 e^{\left[\alpha p - \beta\left(\frac{1}{T_0} - \frac{1}{T_m}\right) + \gamma \frac{p}{T_m}\right]} \tag{64}$$

where z_0 and T_0 are viscosity and temperature at the roll entrance, T_m is the mean temperature of the lubricant film, α, β and γ are lubricant parameters. Figure 57 illustrates the importance of using the correct relationship; the pressure in the roll gap varies widely with the lubricant parameters. Here $\alpha' = \alpha Y$, $\beta' = \dfrac{\beta}{T_0}$ and $\gamma' = \dfrac{\gamma Y}{T_0}$ are dimensionless parameters, and Y is the effective yield stress of the deforming material.

	Lubricant A	Lubricant B
α'	−6·408	−7·05
β'	15·15	15·15
γ'	14·64	16·10

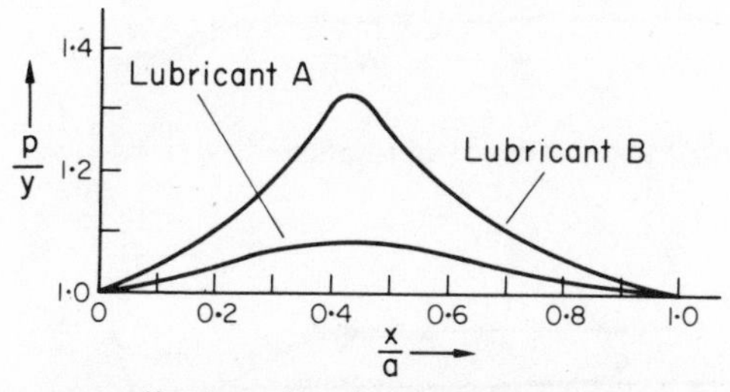

x: co-ordinate in the direction opposite to the lubricant flow
a: width of contact region
p: contact pressure
y: yield stress

Fig. 57. Effect of lubricant parameters on the pressure profile in sheet rolling. (After Cheng, Ref. 97.)

It has been suggested[98] that, in wire drawing with forced lubrication, three possible lubrication conditions can be envisaged. At some critical condition, full fluid lubrication is established (Fig. 58*a*). At an insufficient fluid pressure, from rest up to a critical velocity of up to 300 ft/min in experiments with oil, boundary lubrication exists in the die (Fig. 58*b*), and this might become re-established, e.g. if the viscosity of the oil is lowered by high temperatures at large speeds. In the other extreme, the fluid pressure could become so high that the deformation is partly or fully completed before the wire reaches the die (Fig. 58*c*). Conditions *b* and *c* might become unstable at high speeds. The wire resembling a bamboo stick is produced, with extended smaller diameter matt surfaces alternating with short shiny bands of larger diameter. This "bamboo effect" has also been observed in hydrostatic extrusion.[29] It is thus possible that, in hydrostatic extrusion, under certain as yet unspecified conditions, in a single extrusion, first boundary lubrication, then a mixed lubrication and then full fluid lubrication is present, with changes of billet configuration in the deformation zone or other factors sufficient to bring about a transition from one lubrication condition to another.

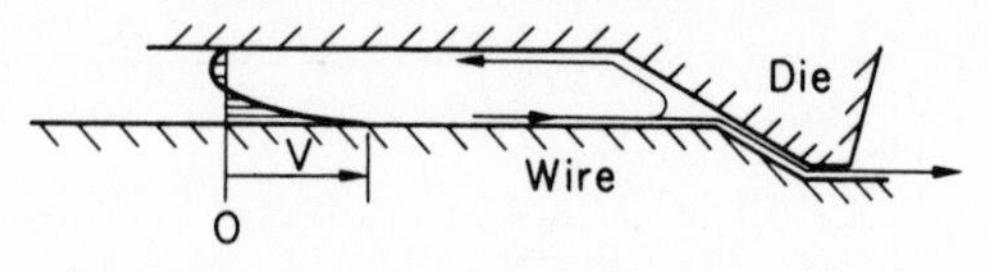

(a) hydrodynamic lubrication

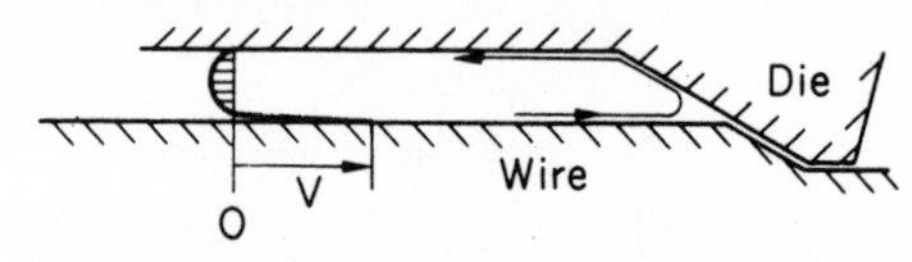

(b) boundary lubrication in die

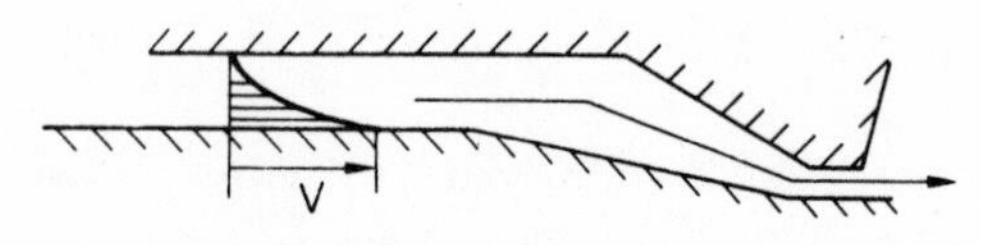

(c) wire deformed in tube

Fig. 58. Flow patterns in wire drawing with forced lubrication. (After Wistreich, Ref. 98.)

While a comparison between hydrostatic extrusion and wire drawing is useful, it is important to appreciate at least one important difference. In wire drawing with a pressure tube the viscous shear force, which operates between the lubricant and wire moving along at high speed, builds up the pressure which separates the deforming material and tool in fluid lubrication. In hydrostatic extrusion, however, a pressurised fluid wedge can be formed between billet and die (Fig. 59) even before there is any billet motion. This pressurised fluid wedge will then assist in developing full fluid or mixed lubrication conditions during extrusion. The effectiveness of p in the development of fluid lubrication is likely to depend on the relative geometry of the die and billet; it might be possible to reduce the critical billet velocity at which fluid (or mixed) lubrication develops if the billet has a smaller cone angle than the die, or by radiusing the usually sharp transition between the conical and parallel parts of the billet.[34] Both methods have the same effect; the pressurised fluid penetrates between the billet/die interface and a reduced extrusion speed might be sufficient to achieve fluid lubrication.

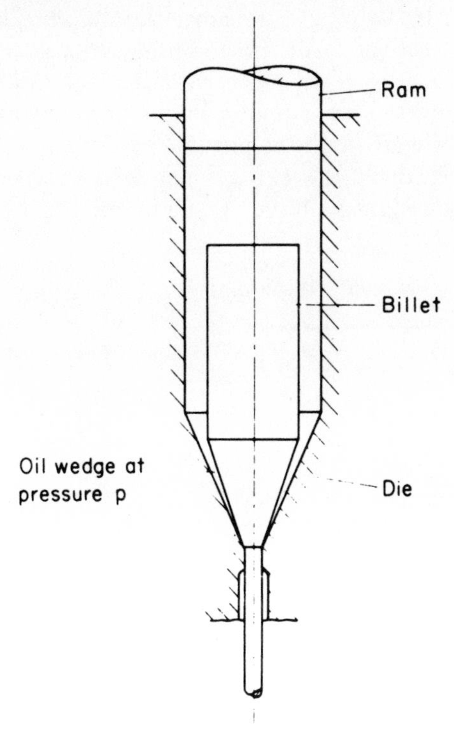

Fig. 59. Pressurised oil wedge between die and stationary billet in hydrostatic extrusion.

There is one more point to consider in hydrostatic extrusion under very high pressures: the viscosity of liquid lubricants increases by a large factor which could also be responsible for the development of fluid or mixed lubrication, where otherwise this would be considered impossible.[99]

This view is reinforced by observations in conventional wire drawing[100] which indicate that, if the die angle is low, separation of the wire and die could occur by a thick film of lubricant even at low speeds. If the surface of the wire or billet is treated by shot-blasting before wire drawing or hydrostatic extrusion, the lubricant retained in these pockets can also play a part in improving lubrication conditions, by helping to separate the die and deforming material effectively. All these considerations seem to indicate that it is by no means certain that full fluid lubrication can develop in orthodox hydrostatic extrusion only at high speeds. It might be possible to achieve such a condition at relatively low extrusion speeds, or when the die pressure is relatively large, as in augmented extrusion;

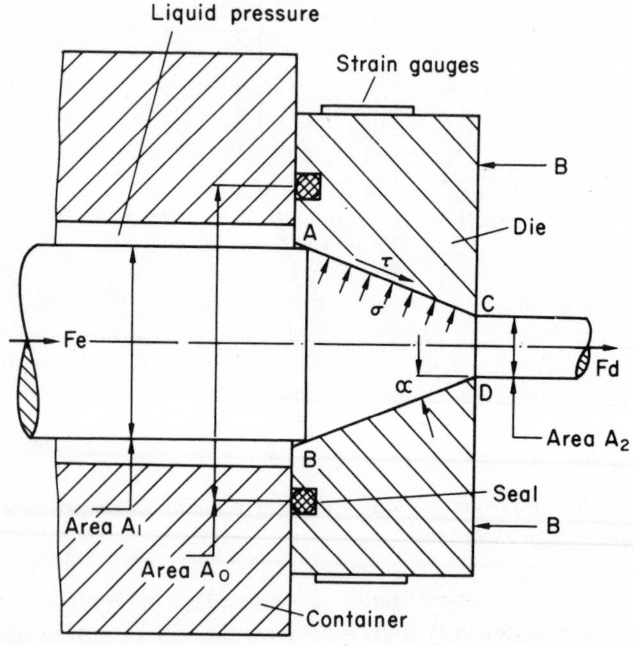

Fig. 60. Forces on the billet and die in hydrostatic extrusion with product augmentation. (*After Parsons* et al., *Ref. 45.*)

the viscosity of the pressure-transmitting liquid, which also acts as a liquid lubricant, could then be of great significance.

Although several methods exist for evaluation of the frictional coefficient in metalworking, it is desirable to establish the lubrication properties of liquids by tests in hydrostatic extrusion itself, if a realistic assessment of their behaviour in the process is required.

In one method, strain gauges are attached to the periphery of the die (Fig. 60) in order to determine the effect of product augmentation on the frictional conditions,[45] the strain gauges being calibrated by applying a known fluid pressure q over the area of the truncated cone. The mean coefficient of friction is then calculated from the formula

$$\mu = \frac{(F_e + F_d)\cos\alpha - q\Delta A}{\sin\alpha(F_e + F_d) + q\Delta A\cot\alpha} \qquad (65)^*$$

The meaning of the symbols is indicated in Fig. 60 and $\Delta A = A_1 - A_2$.

The most interesting results of this work are plotted in Figs. 61 and 62. The simple theory of hydrostatic extrusion leads us to expect that the sum of extrusion pressure plus drawing stress will remain constant (neglecting friction). It can be seen from Fig. 61 that this is not the case; the sum of these two quantities increases for all die angles (except 60° for which there were rather few results) as the drawing stress is decreased in relation to the extrusion pressure. When the ratio (Extrusion Stress)/(Drawing Stress) = 24,000/4000 = 6, the sum reaches a constant maximum value for the 15° and 30° dies. This is illustrated in Fig. 62, in which the friction coefficient is plotted versus this ratio. Values of the friction coefficient are rather high and the authors attribute this to the fact that they did not apply any separate lubricant coating to the billets.

* In the authors' opinion the correct form of equation (65) is

$$\mu = \frac{(F_e + F_d) - q\Delta A}{(F_e + F_d)\tan\alpha + q\Delta A\cot\alpha}$$

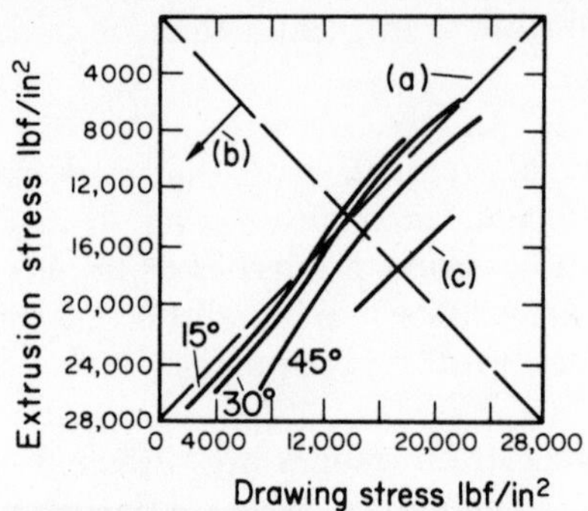

Fig. 61. Correlation between drawing stress and extrusion stress (After Parsons et al., *Ref. 45.)*

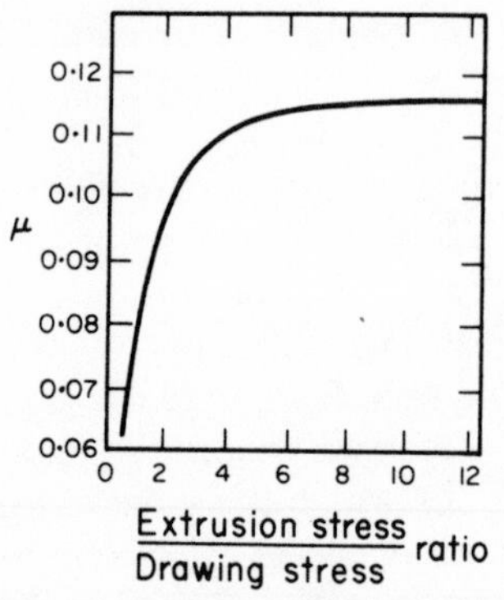

Fig. 62. Variation of friction coefficient for 15° included die angle. Product augmentation. (After Parsons et al., *Ref. 45.)*

In another method[101] the theoretically derived extrusion pressure, given by equations (4) and (4*a*), is used to obtain the coefficient of friction. If either of these equations is differentiated with respect to α and the derivative is equated to zero, the optimum die angle is obtained. Consequently, if in a number of experiments the extrusion pressure is measured at various die angles while the other parameters are kept constant, the optimum die angle is given by the minimum of the pressure versus die angle curves (Fig. 63). This value of the optimum die angle is then used to obtain the coefficient of friction, for various extrusion ratios, and these are shown in Fig. 63 for the assumption given by equation (4). It is interesting to note that, in Fig. 63, μ decreases with increasing die pressure; this effect is quite the opposite to that found by a number of workers in wire drawing and open die extrusion.

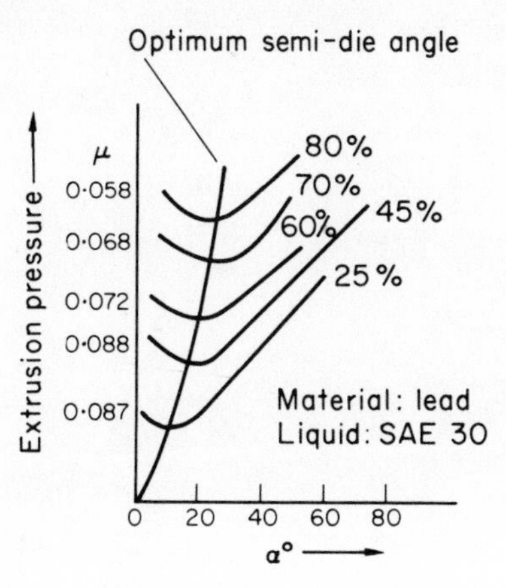

Fig. 63. Optimum semi-die angle and coefficient of friction in orthodox hydrostatic extrusion. (After Evans et al., *Ref. 101.)*

For the design of production hydrostatic extrusion equipment, the compressibility, thermal expansion, thermal conductivity and specific heat of the liquid must also be known.

The definition of compressibility at pressure p is

$$C = \frac{1}{\rho}\frac{d\rho}{dp} = -\frac{1}{V}\frac{dV}{dp} \tag{66}$$

where ρ is density and V is volume, i.e. the volume decreases when density increases. The compressibility of liquids at high pressures is substantial.[102, 103] If, in production equipment, the billet is much smaller than the container bore, a significant amount of work must be expended to compress the liquid and this affects equipment design and the economics of the process. Figure 64 shows that losses owing to this effect are not negligible. The work that must be expended to deform the billet material (plastic work) and to compress the fluid (elastic work) has been calculated for the extrusion of 1 in., 3 in., and 5·75 in. diameter, 24 in. long billets of EN2E steel, from a 6 in. diameter container. The elastic work necessary to deform the billet material and the tool has been neglected. The plastic work was calculated by Pugh's method with $\mu = 0{\cdot}01$. The pressure/compressibility

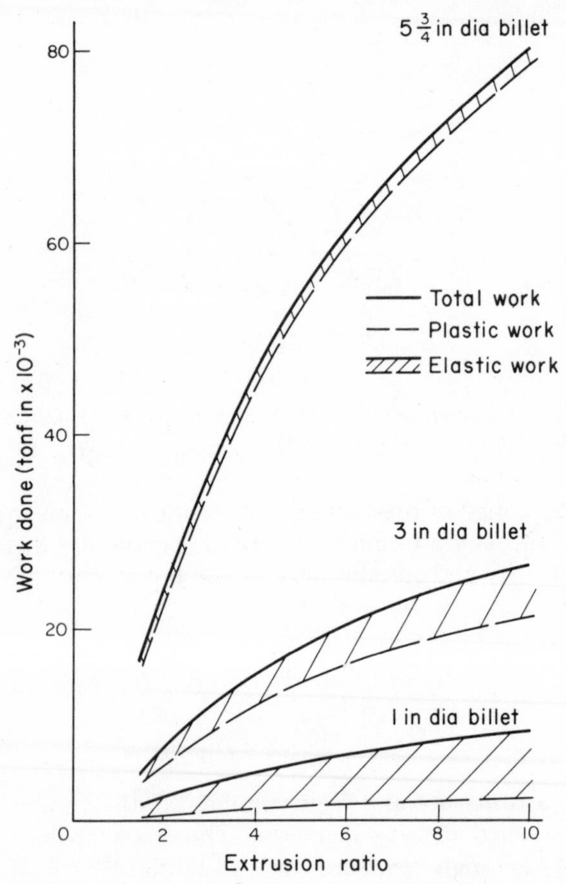

Fig. 64. Plastic and elastic components of the total work in hydrostatic extrusion.

characteristics of ethyl acetate have been used;[103] ethyl acetate remained liquid at the maximum pressure of 40,000 atm. (approximately 40 kbar) applied in that work. The stroke of the plunger was assumed to be the minimum necessary to attain the required pressures, without the plunger contacting the billet. Figure 64 illustrates the manner in which the total work increases if a substantial volume of liquid must be compressed, because the billet is smaller in diameter than the container bore. The same obviously applies in the case when the container is longer than the billet, or if two containers are used in augmented extrusion (Fig. 8).

Bridgman[103] showed that a number of liquids do not solidify up to 40,000 atm. pressure; this indicates that the extension of hydrostatic extrusion to this very high pressure region does not depend on the pressure transmitting properties of the available liquids, but on their other characteristics and on equipment design.

The density ρ_t is also a function of temperature t in the form

$$\rho_t = \rho_0[1 - \beta(t - t_0)] \qquad (67)$$

where β is the coefficient of thermal expansion which varies with viscosity[104] and ρ_0 is density at temperature t_0.

Experimental relationships on the thermal conductivity and specific heat of liquids are given, for example, in Ref. 105. These properties are important in equipment design, since the temperature rise affects stress conditions, which could affect die wear and the fatigue properties of the container.

It has already been mentioned that no systematic investigation has yet been published either into friction in hydrostatic extrusion or into the selection of fluids. However, a considerable amount of experimental work has been carried out into the effects of selected fluids and lubricants on extrusion pressure, surface finish of the product, etc. and this is outlined in Chapter 5.

4.5 INSTRUMENTATION

In hydrostatic extrusion and related experimental work the measurement of liquid pressures from say 1 to 30 kbar is required, the rate of pressure change being sufficiently low to be detected by most "static" devices.

Pressure gauges are normally divided into two categories: primary and secondary gauges. Primary gauges, which measure pressure in terms of basic units, are used to calibrate secondary gauges, or to determine fixed points on the high pressure scale by detecting the phase changes or polymorphic transitions of pure substances, which are then used to calibrate secondary gauges. Secondary gauges give an indication of pressure by detecting the change of some material property, such as electrical resistance, with pressure, or by measuring strain on the application of pressure, etc. In hydrostatic extrusion it is convenient to use secondary pressure gauges: those which proved most useful in the process and in related experimental work (such as in the testing of high pressure containers) will now be discussed briefly.

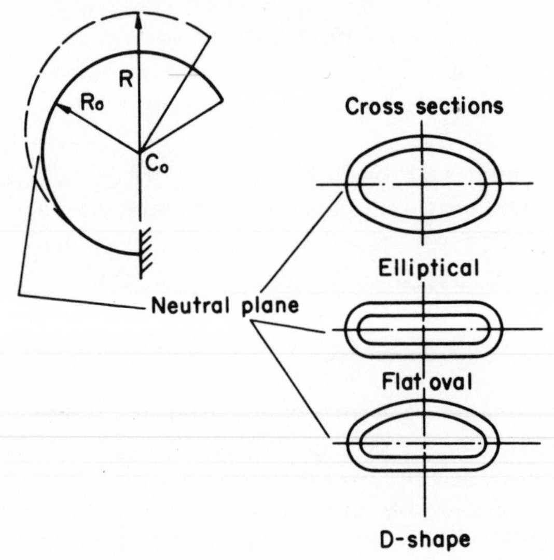

Fig. 65. Deformation of the Bourdon tube and its various possible cross-sections. (After Mason, Ref. 106.)

The pressure gauge known as the Bourdon tube was invented in 1849 by Schinz and marketed by Bourdon.[106] It is made of a flattened tube of elliptical, flat-oval or D-shape cross section (Fig. 65). It is bent into a C-shape (as illustrated) or, to increase sensitivity, into a helix or flat spiral. It is sealed at one end and connected usually via a toothed quadrant to a pointer and to the pressure source at the other end. When pressure is applied, the cross-section changes towards the circular: the inside wall moves towards the centre of curvature C_0 and the outside wall moves away from C_0. As a result, tensile stresses are generated in the outside and compressive stresses in the inside wall; the combined effect is a bending moment which increases the radius of curvature from R_0 to R.

Statistical data indicate that the fatigue life of the Bourdon tube is limited.[106] For example, for gauges rated at 1000 lbf/in² (69·0 bar) it rarely exceeds 10^5 pressure cycles, but it is often as low as 5 to 9000 cycles. Hysteresis and temperature effects partly account for an often limited accuracy, which might vary between 0·2 and 5% of the full scale from one gauge to another.[107] This, together with inertia and fatigue effects limit the usefulness of the Bourdon tube to steady and relatively low pressures, up to 100,000 lbf/in² (6·9 kbar).

In place of the Bourdon tube, the pressure sensing element could be an eccentrically bored thick walled tube. Owing to the eccentricity, the pressure generates a bending moment displacing the tip, which can then be used to move a pointer in front of a calibrated dial. The use of autofrettaged tubes allows such gauges to be built for pressures up to 200,000 lbf/in² (13·8 kbar). The limitations of this gauge are similar to those of the Bourdon tube.

The bulk modulus cell is a thick-walled tube, closed at one end and sealed into an opening in a pressure vessel.[108] Under the effect of pressure the stem moves axially outwards (Fig. 66). The magnitude of this movement depends on the size of the tube, the elastic moduli of its material and the pressure in the vessel; it can be made sufficiently large to permit detection by several accurate methods. Bulk modulus cells are available for pressures up to 200,000 lbf/in^2 (13·8 kbar). Hysteresis and temperature effects could influence its accuracy: one operating between 0 and 200,000 lbf/in^2 (13·8 kbar) exhibited 0·5% hysteresis effect, while a temperature rise from 0°C to 77°C caused a reading shift of about 2%.[108]

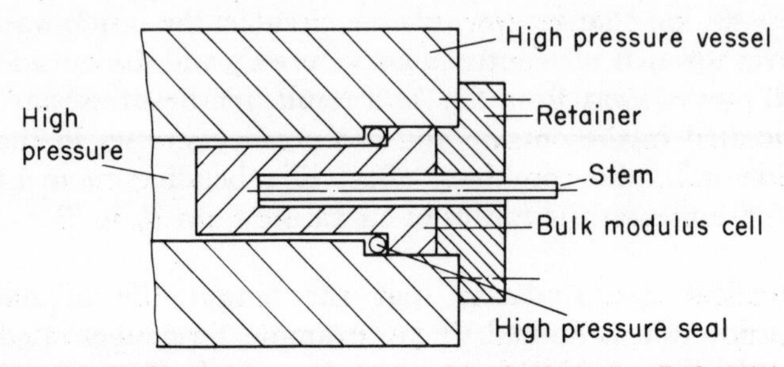

Fig. 66. Bulk modulus cell. (*After Newhall* et al., *Ref. 107.*)

Electrical resistance strain gauges can also be used for the measurement of high liquid pressures, either by attaching them to the outside of a tube under internal pressure or to the bore when the tube is under external pressure.[69] The tube can be made with one end closed and the other sealed into the high pressure vessel, or it may be made part of the high pressure system, if the pressurised liquid is piped.

When the pressure p acts in the bore and the strain gauges are attached circumferentially to the outside, the measured elastic hoop strain is

$$e_\theta = \frac{p(2 - \nu)}{E(K^2 - 1)} \tag{68}$$

If the gauges are fitted parallel to the axis of the tube then the measured axial strain is

$$e_z = \frac{p(1 - 2\nu)}{E(K^2 - 1)} \tag{69}$$

With the strain gauges attached to the bore and pressure

p applied to the outside of the tube, the corresponding strains are

$$e_\theta = K^2 \frac{p(2 - \nu)}{E(K^2 - 1)}; \qquad e_z = K^2 \frac{p(1 - 2\nu)}{E(K^2 - 1)} \qquad (70)$$

which are larger, by the factor K^2, than the strains detected by strain gauges fixed to the outside of the tube. This could be an advantage, together with the possible greater safety if the pressure is applied to the outside. For the strain gauge methods, the maximum pressure is about the same as for the eccentric tube and for the bulk modulus cell, since all these methods employ thick-walled tubes to contain and detect the pressure. Hysteresis and fatigue effects are also common limitations, but temperature effects on the strain gauge readings can be eliminated.

In hydrostatic extrusion, probably the most useful secondary pressure gauges are those which detect the change of electrical resistance with pressure in metals, commonly in manganin, an alloy which contains about 80 % Cu, 10 % Ni and 5 % each of Mn and Fe. The manganin gauge is a small coil of fine gauge wire (available in a wide range of sizes from 0·025 to 0·50 mm nominal diameter) non-inductively wound, usually onto a bobbin and subjected to the pressure to be measured. It is small and compact, and the electrical leads can be taken out easily from the pressure vessel by one of several methods described later; it is not necessary, therefore, to have threaded connections for attachment of additional pieces of apparatus. Hysteresis effects are present, but they can be reduced to an acceptable level by "seasoning" the manganin, i.e. by subjecting the wound gauge to repeated applications of pressure as high as, or higher than the maximum pressure expected to be measured, followed by a stress relieving heat treatment. In service, the manganin coil is subjected to pressure, and the increase in electrical resistance is measured by connecting the gauge as one arm of a Wheatstone bridge, or some similar method. The electrical signals can be easily recorded, and the manganin gauge has become invaluable in fatigue work, particularly since its life is practically unlimited with a suitable design, provided the pressure transmitting medium remains liquid.[48]

The use of manganin for pressure measurement has been suggested by Lisell[109] and developed by Bridgman;[110] it is being used in practically all high pressure laboratories. The change of resistance is linear at 10 kbar within about 0·1% and at 30 kbar within 0·15%. Temperature has an effect similar to that of pressure; the change in the pressure coefficient is 0·013% per °C at 1000 bar.[111] To eliminate the influence of temperature the use of two manganin coils has been suggested; these are placed in two separate chambers of a single steel block, one of which is pressurised and the other is at atmospheric pressure. The ratio of resistances of the two coils is measured in a modified Wheatstone bridge after the heat generated by the compression of the fluid has been dissipated through the steel block, when both coils are at the same temperature. However, the usefulness of this method is in some doubt, because the temperature coefficient of resistance varies with pressure. According to one authority (reference 112, discussion) it has been found zero at about 29°C at atmospheric pressure and at about 39°C at 8 kbar.

A further problem with the manganin gauge is that its pressure coefficient may change between different supplies of the material by as much as 2%,[112] and the temperature coefficient of resistance also varies from batch to batch. Variations occur even when the gauges are made from the same length of wire. It is important, therefore, to calibrate each gauge separately against a primary standard or to compare it with fixed points on the high pressure scale.

Several methods are used for making the electrical connections with manganin gauges, thermocouples or strain gauges. Amagat[113] used a steel cone, insulated and sealed by a layer of hard rubber or ivory (Fig. 67). A similar arrangement is still being used by many investigators in the form illustrated in Fig. 68. A sintered ceramic cone is lapped into a hole in the plunger or other part of the high pressure equipment, and a conical hardened steel terminal is in turn lapped into the bore of the ceramic insulator. Internal and external leads are then soldered to the terminal. The unsupported areas of the insulator and terminal ensure satisfactory sealing.

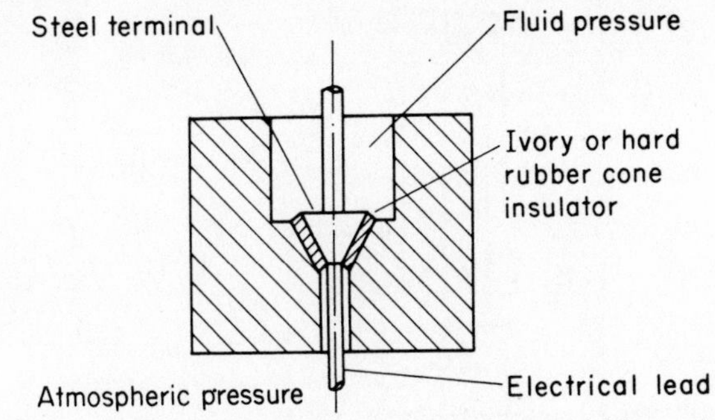

Fig. 67. Amagat's terminal and insulator. (*After Amagat, Ref. 113.*)

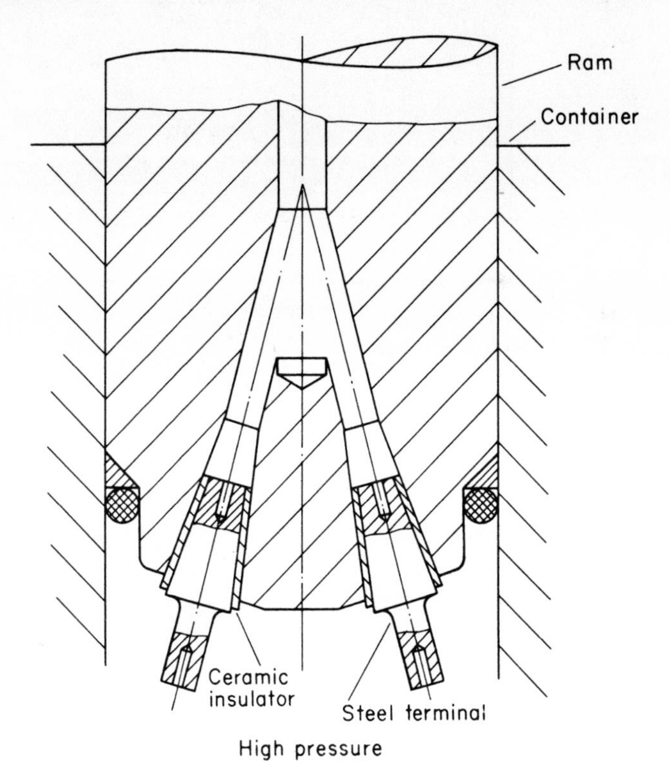

Fig. 68. Steel terminal and ceramic insulator. (*After Pugh, Ref. 5.*)

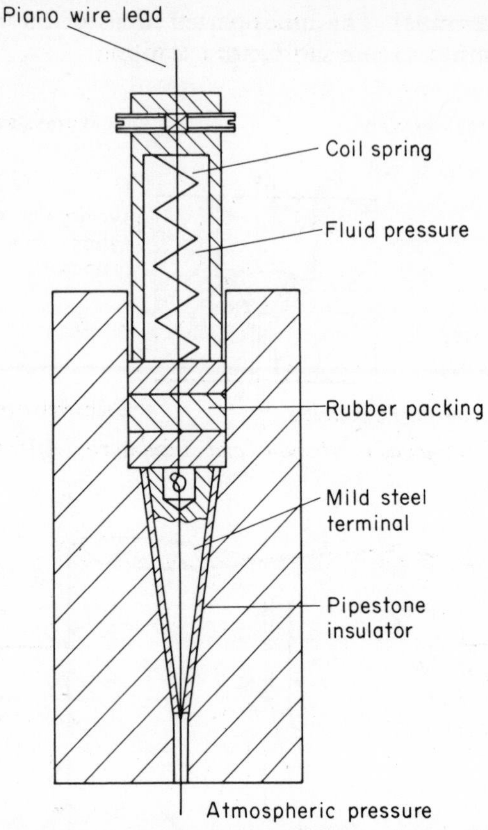

Fig. 69. Bridgman's terminal and insulator. (After Bridgman, Ref. 114.)

For pressures up to 30 kbar Bridgman[114] used the design illustrated in Fig. 69. In this, the conical insulator is only 0·005 in thick; it is made of pipestone with an angle of 15°. Friction along the interface gradually diminishes the stresses towards the apex, until they become zero both in the mild steel terminal and in the insulator, thus neither of them will be sheared through and expelled by the pressure. The electrical lead, made of 0·013 in. diameter piano wire, is knotted to prevent it being pulled through the hole in the terminal. Sealing is now by rubber discs which are made to a larger diameter than the hole to ensure that, even after a volume reduction of 27% under 30 kbar pressure, they are still of sufficient size to prevent a leak. A coil spring is used to prevent the oversize rubber disc from slipping out of the hole. On the low pressure side, insulation has been achieved by winding a silk thread around the wire.

A multi-electrode terminal has been developed[138] using a different application of the same principle (Fig. 70). A slotted conical steel plug of 0·25 in maximum diameter and 15° included angle is inserted into a matching hole in the plunger, with insulated copper wires bonded into the slots with an epoxy resin. The friction between the coated and bonded wires and slots prevents the leads from being expelled by the pressure. This method is particularly convenient for taking out a greater number of leads from the vessel, without substantially weakening the plunger or other components to which this device is fitted.[138]

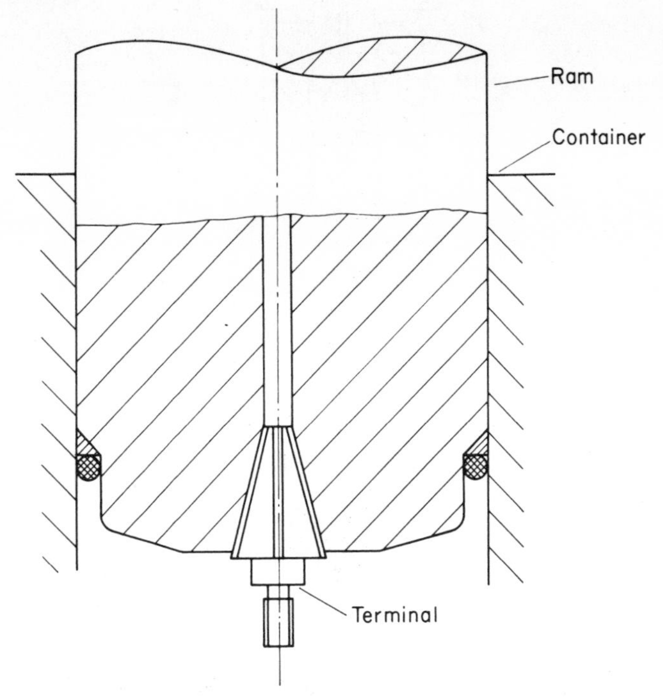

Fig. 70. Multi-electrode terminal. (After Chandler, Ref. 115.)

4.6 SUMMARY OF EXISTING EXPERIMENTAL AND PRODUCTION APPARATUS

Both monobloc [23, 27–29, 32, 38, 52] and compound [5, 25, 35, 61, 117–19] containers are widely used in experimental and production equipment, the former mainly for their simplicity of construction at up to 10 kbar pressures, the latter where higher pressures are required, up to 30 kbar.

Two types of monobloc apparatus have been used in one of the early works.[23] In Fig. 71 the monobloc vessel

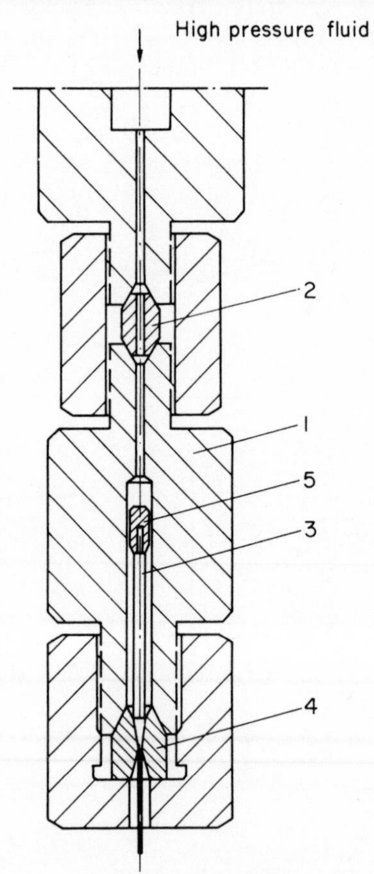

Fig. 71. Monobloc vessel using piped fluid for orthodox hydrostatic extrusion. (After Beresnev et al., *Ref. 23.)*

[1] is sealed by a ground steel cone [2] and the high pressure fluid is piped to the specimen [3]. To prevent a sudden release of pressure and the violent ejection of the specimen, the die [4] is closed at the end of the extrusion by a hardened steel plug [5].

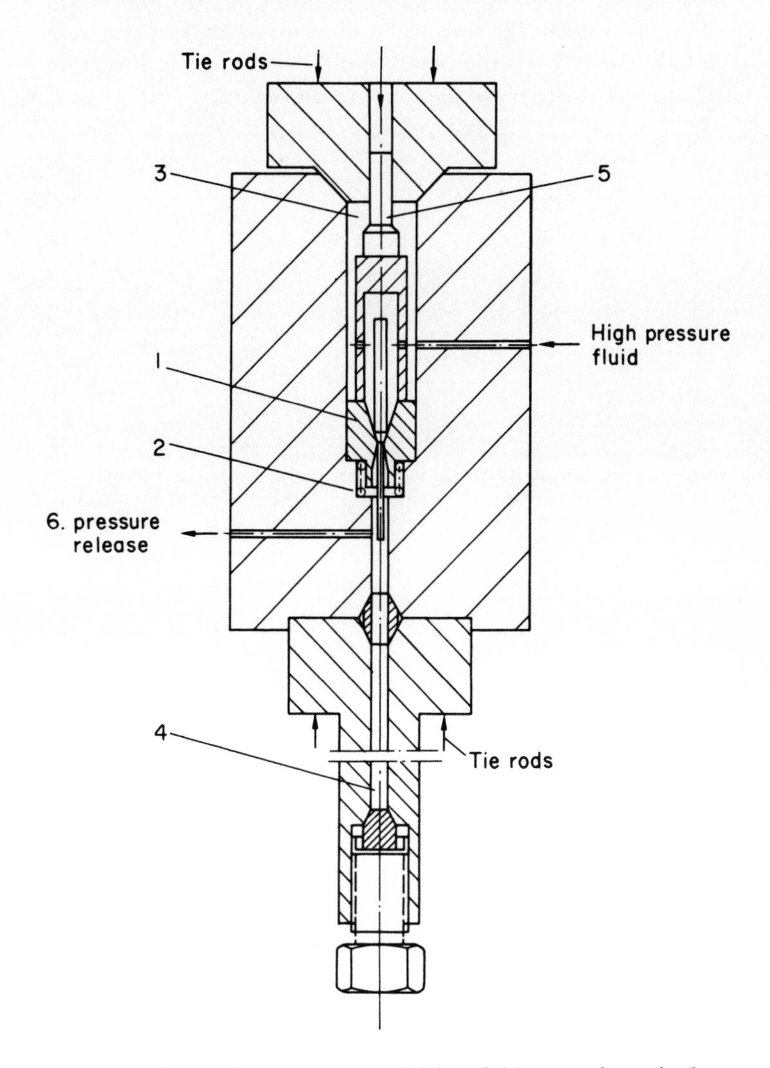

Fig. 72. Monobloc vessel for fluid-to-fluid extrusion. (*After Beresnev* et al., *Ref. 23.*)

For differential pressure extrusion the equipment outlined in Fig. 72 was used. Initially the die [1] is kept floating by a spring [2] and the fluid is piped to pressurise the upper [3] and lower [4] chambers simultaneously. A plunger [5] then forces down the die on to a shoulder to seal between the two chambers, thus separating them. The pressure in the lower chamber is reduced by opening a valve [6]. When the pressure difference between the two chambers is large enough, extrusion begins.

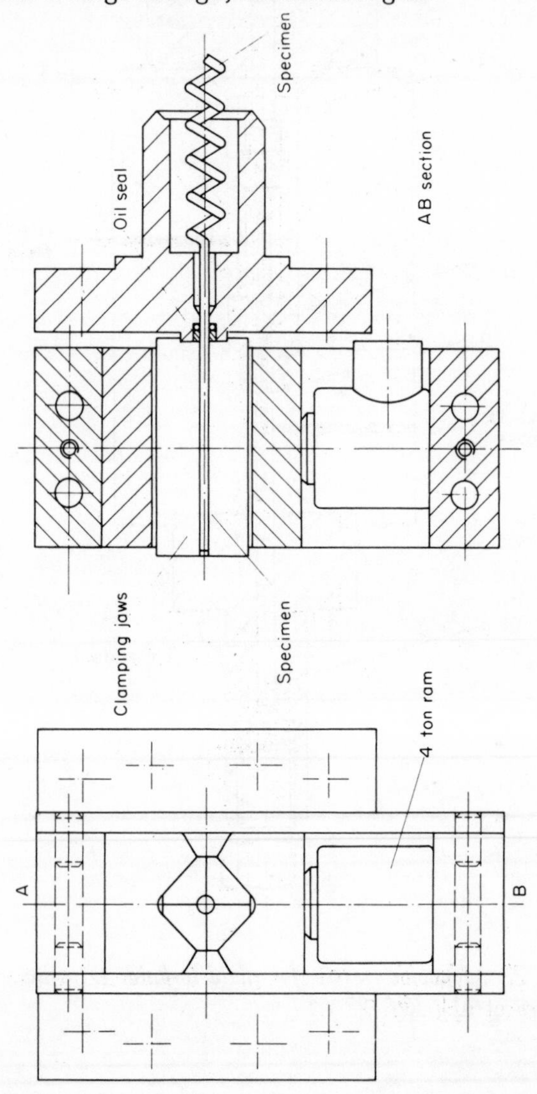

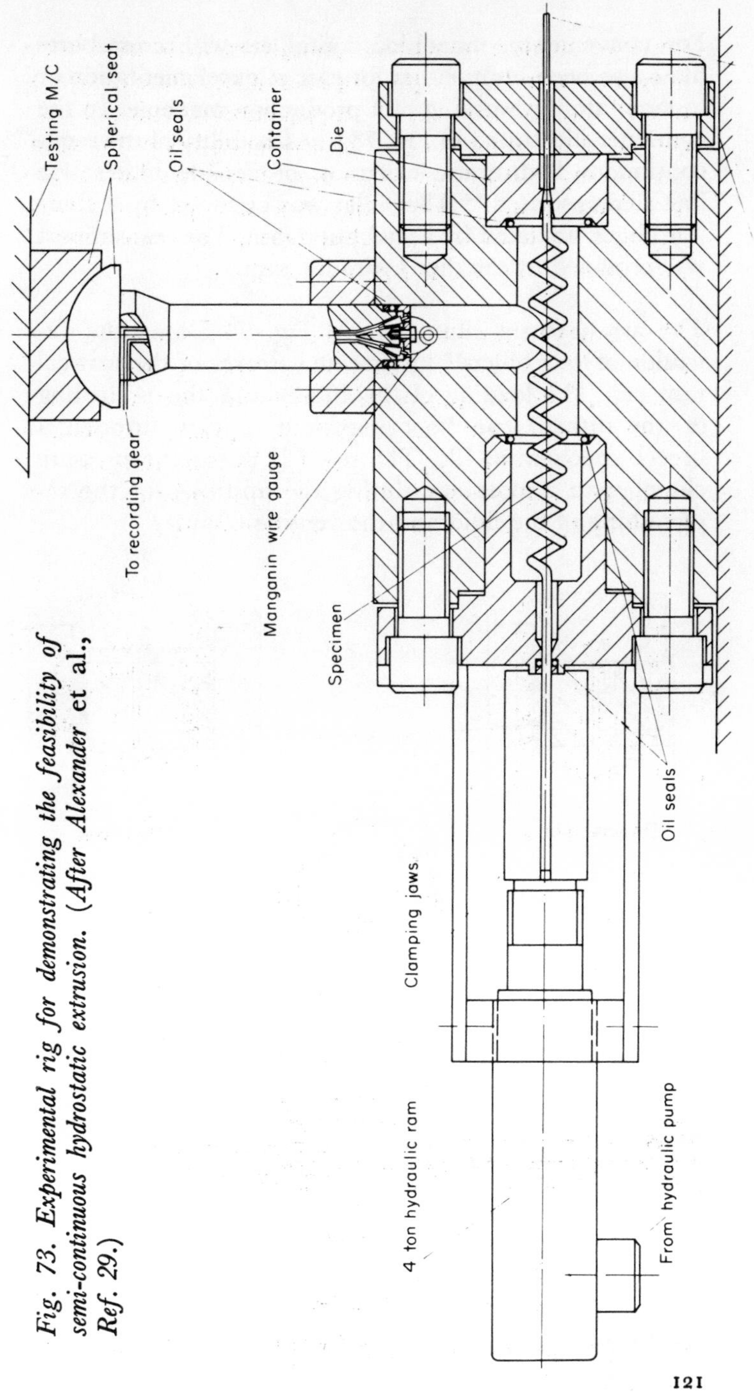

Fig. 73. Experimental rig for demonstrating the feasibility of semi-continuous hydrostatic extrusion. (After Alexander et al., *Ref.* 29.)

For convenience, monobloc containers with cross bores have also been built, either for ease of experimentation or to facilitate the working of a production machine. In the container illustrated in Fig. 73, the feasibility of the semi-continuous hydrostatic extrusion of flexible billets was first demonstrated.[29] The billet was clamped by a four-jaw chuck actuated by a hydraulic ram. The seal support was provided by another hydraulic ram.

The arrangement illustrated in Fig. 74 allows the extrusion of long billets[28] by repeated strokes of the vertical ram [1]. The loading of the billets and the unloading of the discard can be carried out quickly through a breech mechanism [2]. The seal [3] opens the pressure chamber to atmosphere during the upstroke for the replenishing of the fluid and the venting of air.

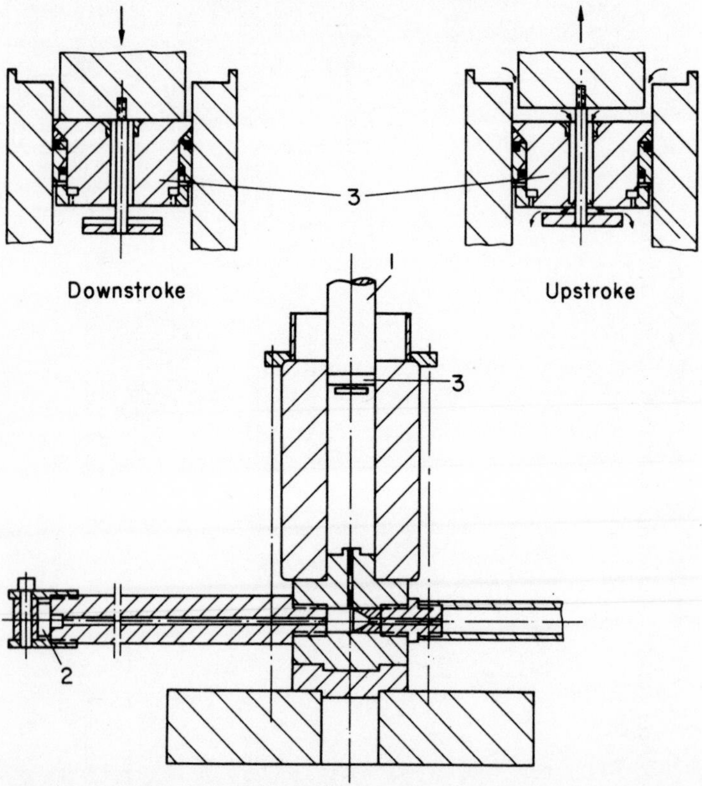

Fig. 74. Production unit for orthodox hydrostatic extrusion. (After Green, Ref. 28.)

A monobloc container is used in an experimental unit for the development of semi-continuous hydrostatic extrusion.[32] A schematic drawing of this unit is shown in Fig. 75. The feed stock is delivered from the pit of a 300 tonf hydraulic press and is clamped by the sizing tube (Fig. 52). The main ram is then lowered to pressurise the fluid in the container with the tubular pressurising plunger. When extrusion pressure is reached, the feed plunger rises to permit extrusion to commence and the pressurising plunger automatically withdraws to maintain constant fluid pressure during the extrusion stroke. The feed stops after 3 in stroke, and the main ram lifts to de-pressurise the fluid. The feed stock is then unclamped and retained with the check clamps and the feed plunger retracts to collect new feed stock. The cycle is then repeated.

The basic principle of other semi-continuous hydrostatic extrusion machines is similar and will not be described here. The main difference is in the clamping and sealing device; suggestions include (1) collapsing tubes (Fig. 51)—usually slit axially and covered by a rubber sheath—which clamp the feed stock over their bore diameter when this is reduced owing to their outside being subjected to the fluid pressure during extrusion,[37, 95] or (2) the use of a clamp in the form of a thick-walled tube made of segments being held together without gaps (Fig. 52), the billet material expanding into it to develop the interfacial friction which prevents the ejection of the billet.[32] This seemingly minor difference is very important: the latter device produces only negligible clamping marks on the billet material and the clamping of billets with wide tolerances should be possible. Neither of these devices has yet been developed to a stage at which its technical success could be judged with confidence.

The simplest compound container is the two cylinder taper support construction of Bridgman (Fig. 32); this is particularly useful for experimental work. The usual general arrangement is illustrated in Fig. 1.[5, 61], the top and bottom plungers being actuated by the rams of a hydraulic press.

Two containers, each made of two shrink-fit cylinders, are used in the UKAEA/Fielding & Platt Hydrostat 1600/80 (Fig. 76). This is an automatic machine for hydrostatic extrusion either with or without billet augmentation, at pressures up to 12 kbar.[117] The augmentation load is supplied by the out-of-balance force resulting from the different areas of the billet and pressure containers; this can be reduced by withholding the pressure container with the auxiliary ram. The augmenting plunger is also a thick-walled pressure vessel with high pressure tubing autofrettaged into its bore as a liner.

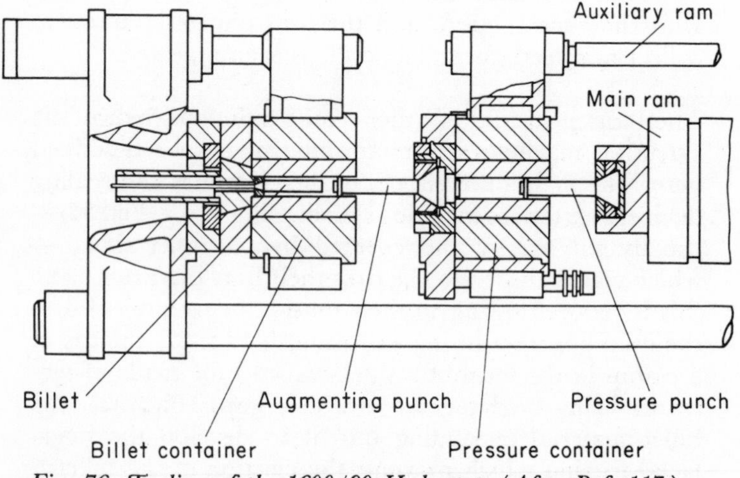

Fig. 76. Tooling of the 1600/80 Hydrostat. (After Ref. 117.)

Containers of three-component shrink-fit construction are used in experimental work at pressures up to 20 kbar.[25, 35] In one case, electrical resistance heaters on the outside of the container are used to heat the fluid for hydrostatic extrusion at elevated temperatures.[25]

In another design (Fig. 77) the container is built from two compound cylinders with a fluid interlayer between them.[118] The inner compound cylinder consists of a thin-walled liner with segmented and solid support cylinders. The outer compound cylinder is of dual, shrink-fit construction. When the liner is pressurised, its bore expands and high pressure fluid leaks past the plunger. The fluid is fed into the annular space between the two compound cylinders. It is claimed that the magnitude of this interfacial fluid pressure can be controlled, since the clearance between the plunger and liner tends to zero as the interfacial pressure increases; thus, an equilibrium condition is established. This container is said to support 34 kbar pressure for an unlimited number of cycles without failure.

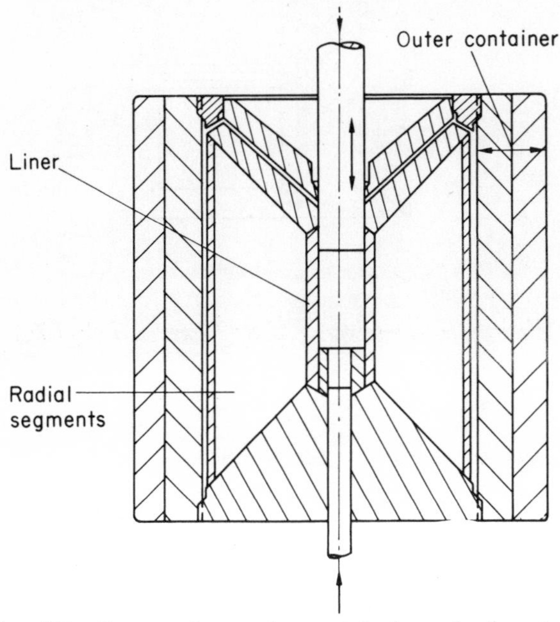

Fig. 77. Compound container with dynamic interfacial fluid pressure. (After Fuchs, Ref. 118.)

Wire-wound containers are used both in experimental and production equipment.[119, 120] A thick-walled cylinder is pre-stressed by winding wire on its outside with tension. Two further cylinders pressed into this assembly (Fig. 78) ensure that there are no tensile hoop stresses in the inner cylinders when at pressure. It is claimed that, if required, the liner can be replaced *in situ* by forcing it out with the press ram. A new liner can then be forced in without disturbing the rest of the assembly, and with sufficient interference to ensure once more that there are no tensile hoop stresses in the liner under the maximum bore pressure. This container is supplied as part of a production machine for pressures up to 20 kbar.

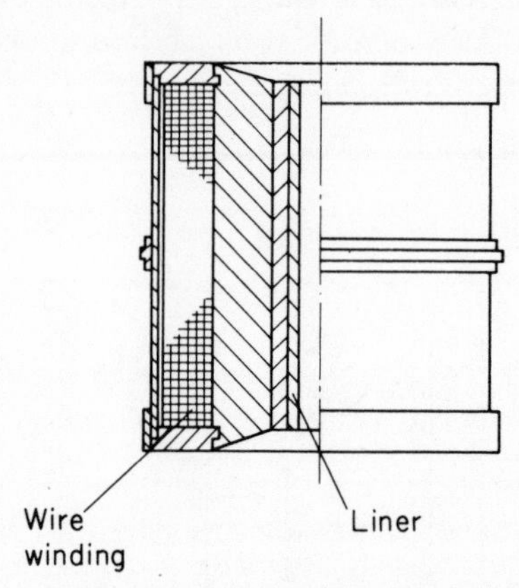

Fig. 78. Wire wound container. (*After Johnsson, Ref. 120.*)

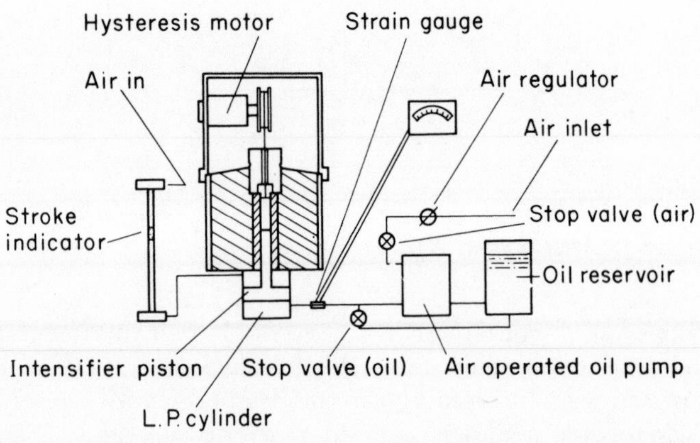

Fig. 79. Wire extrusion machine. (*After Low* et al., *Ref. 34.*)

A wire extrusion machine was developed using a shrink fit container of dual construction for pressures up to 18 kbar.[34] An air-hydro pump supplies oil to an intensifier which generates the required container pressure (Fig. 79). Copper wires down to 0·002 in were extruded with product augmentation. At 10 kbar pressure, 0·011 in diameter copper wire was extruded in one operation to 0·005 in diameter at speeds of up to 1500 ft/min. This wire size could be further reduced to 0·002 in in lengths of up to 1500 ft.

5. Experimental Results

5.1 EXTRUSION PRESSURE

In the first recorded experimental work on hydrostatic extrusion Bridgman extruded copper with kerosene as pressure transmitting medium.[4] He observed that the extrusion pressure was roughly proportional to the reduction in area and, at higher reductions, the metal would "spit out in gulps" instead of emerging smoothly, or "break along diagonal shear planes" at the mouth of the die. Another problem was that, if emergence was too rapid, the product would become excessively hot, possibly causing self-annealing and loss of hardness.

Beresnev and his co-workers found that, by suitable choice of the pressure transmitting medium, the troubles experienced by Bridgman can be eliminated.[23] They also pointed out that the extrusion pressure is influenced by the choice of liquid, as shown in Table 2.

Table 2[23]

PRESSURE TRANSMITTING LIQUID	MEAN PRESSURE AT THE BEGINNING OF EXTRUSION ($kg\ cm^{-2}$ approx. bar)
Hypoid oil	3750
Water + hypoid oil on billet	5000
Water	5450
Transformer oil	5500
Transformer oil + paraffin (0·5 + 0·5)	6500
Transformer oil + paraffin + oleic acid (0·49 + 0·49 + 0·02)	6450
Paraffin	6900
Benzene	6900
Methyl alcohol	6075
Ethyl alcohol	6450

A layer of fluid on the extrudates was observed, and the initial machining marks on the billets remained visible on the product; from this, it was concluded that a layer of liquid separated the metal from the die during extrusion, i.e. some form of fluid lubrication was present. Aluminium gave the most satisfactory results when it was extruded with water as a pressure transmitting medium, with a thin layer of hypoid oil over the billet. Good results were also recorded with 1 : 2 mixture of paraffin and transformer oil and, since this was also a suitable liquid for their high pressure pumps, Beresnev and his colleagues used this mixture in most of their experiments.

Another of their observations was that the extrusion speed increased with pressure, indicating that the pressure to start extrusion must have been higher than the steady state pressure. The larger elastic energy of the compressed liquid accelerated the product to higher velocities with increasing pressures. To measure extrusion pressures they used a "manometer" (probably a Bourdon tube) which has a relatively slow response to pressure fluctuations. This must be the reason why no pressure/displacement curves can be found in their papers, while the existence of pressure fluctuations during extrusion was correctly predicted by them.

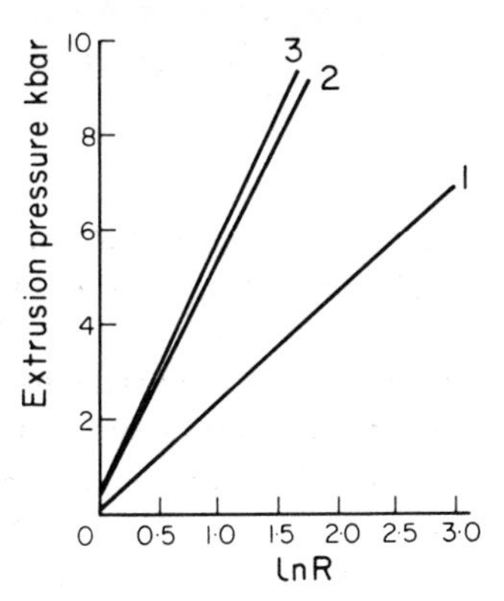

Fig. 80. Relationship between pressure and extrusion ratio. 1. Pure aluminium. 2. Copper. 3. Duralumin. (After Beresnev et al., *Ref. 23.)*

Various metals showed linear relationship between extrusion pressure and logarithmic extrusion ratios. For 40° die semi-angle this is shown in Fig. 80. For various metals the extrusion pressure was at a minimum when the semi-die angle was about 15°: their results are illustrated in Fig. 81.

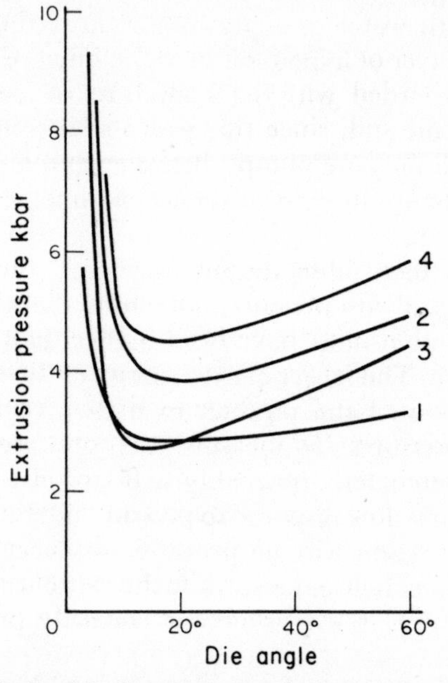

Fig. 81. Relationship between extrusion pressure and die angle. 1. Pure aluminium. 2. M2. 3. DIM. 4. AMg. (*After Beresnev* et al., *Ref. 23.*)

At about the same time, Pugh and his co-workers obtained similar results at the National Engineering Laboratory, U.K. They and many others used manganin gauges and electrical methods for recording extrusion pressure, and were able to detect variations in the pressure during extrusion. In most cases, a distinct difference between the initial and steady state extrusion pressures was recorded as illustrated in Fig. 82.[25] Furthermore, often a stick-slip behaviour and pressure fluctuation accompanied by a poor product appearance (bamboo effect) was observed. This stick-slip is the result of unstable lubrication conditions as was described in Section 4.4. The conditions under which this can develop are not yet clear, but the type and amount of fluid, the rate of pressurisation, the extruded material, the die angle and extrusion ratio, or a combination of these seem to be responsible.

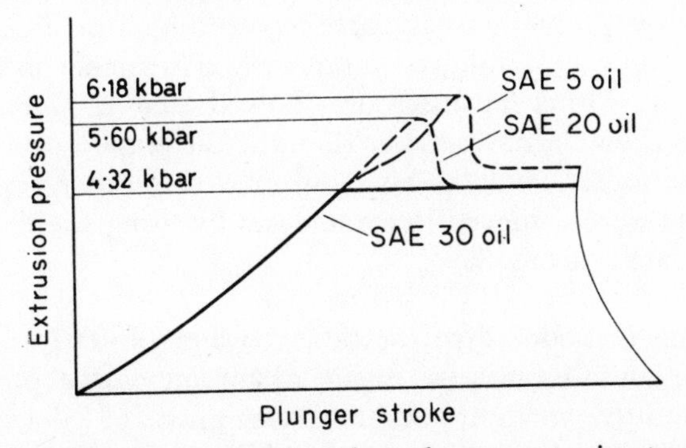

Fig. 82. Initial pressure peak and steady-state extrusion pressures with various fluids. (*After Fiorentino* et al., *Ref. 82.*)

When Dural billets of 1 in diameter and 4 in parallel length, tapered to fit a 45° angle die, were extruded at a ratio of 4, with a 4 : 1 mixture of glycerine and glycol as pressure transmitting fluid[34] there was a marked pressure fluctuation (Fig. 83). Some improvement was achieved by reducing the volume of the fluid and by using sandblasted

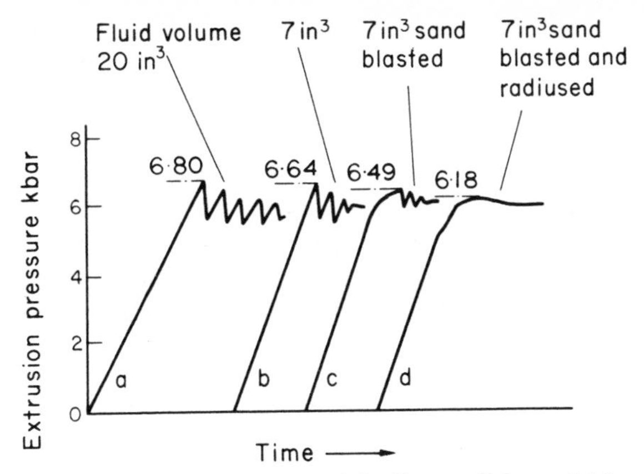

Fig. 83. Pressure trace under stick-slip conditions. (*After Low* et al., *Ref. 34.*)

billets. The pressure fluctuation was completely eliminated and the peak pressure reduced when the usually sharp transition between the parallel and conical parts of the sandblasted billet was radiused, indicating a smooth development of favourable lubrication conditions; these were due probably to an early separation of the billet and die by a layer of fluid, as was described in connection with Fig. 59. Other investigators showed that a billet nose angle a few degrees smaller than the die angle[62] or a compound billet angle[121] also improve conditions. Similar results were achieved in some cases by using the damper illustrated in Fig. 3.

In the orthodox hydrostatic extrusion of 0·07 in diameter aluminium wire, using castor oil as the pressure transmitting medium, at an extrusion ratio of 7·4 a steady state pressure of 4·2 kbar developed; this was followed by fluctuating pressures with peaks of 10·5 kbar[35]. For copper at a ratio of 2·9, the corresponding values were 5·4 kbar and 11 kbar respectively. No stick-slip was found in the extrusion of 0·25 in diameter rods of the same material under identical conditions, indicating a size effect. The pressure fluctuation could be eliminated by the application of a thin layer of graphite grease on the billet. Stick-slip could also be eliminated by augmentation, whether the load is applied to the billet or to the product.

In hydrostatic extrusion, the fluid transmits pressure and could act as a lubricant. The pressure transmitting characteristics of a number of fluids were investigated by measuring load on the pressurising plunger and pressure in the fluid simultaneously.[35] The results are shown in Fig. 84. Ideally, the punch pressure and the fluid pressure measured by a manganin gauge should be identical. By plotting corresponding values, the deviation of the curves from the 45° straight line indicates that pressure is not transmitted effectively. Up to 50 tonf/in^2 (7·7 kbar) all the fluids investigated are quite satisfactory. At about 20 kbar, the divergence of all curves from the straight line, is quite significant with the exception of castor oil and a 4 : 1 mixture of glycerine and ethylene glycol.

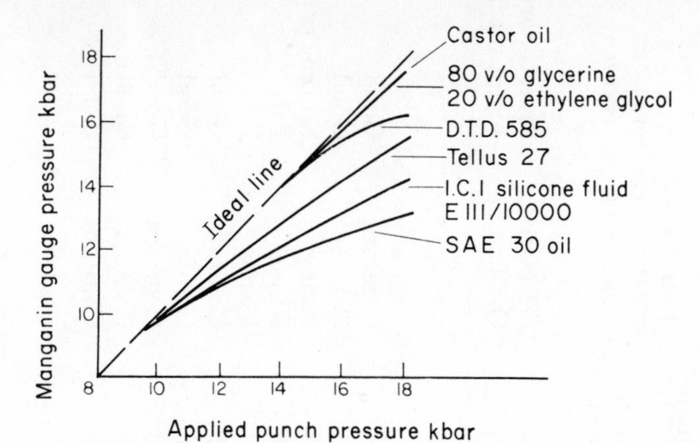

Fig. 84. Behaviour of pressure transmitting fluids. (*After Lowe* et al., *Ref. 35.*)

Various materials were extruded using a number of fluids and billet coatings to find the best combination. Copper and commercially pure titanium were chosen as typical metals of low and high tendency to gall on the die.[35] The results, shown in Table 3, indicate that for copper the choice of fluid little affects the results, but for titanium the fluid and lubricant make significant difference in extrusion conditions.

Subsequently, several alloys were extruded from a 45° die at reductions from 1·2 to 30 to give products of 0·4 in. to 0·25 in. diameter. The pressure transmitting fluid was castor oil, the billets were uncoated except the niobium, titanium and zirconium alloys which were coated with Trilac 45. The results fitted equation (10) in the form

$$p = a + b \ln R \qquad (10a)$$

Values of a and b are given in Table 4. Similar results obtained by other workers for various materials, pressure transmitting media, lubricants and die angles may be found in the references. A survey of the experimental results obtained at the National Engineering Laboratory, together with some results of Russian and American workers, is given by Pugh.[122] It has also been shown[123] that the experimental relationship (10a) holds also for two intermetallic compounds (CuZn and TiNi), at least for small extrusion ratios.

Table 3[35]

BILLET MATERIAL	BILLET COATING	FLUID	EXTRUSION PRESSURE ($tonf/in^2$) BREAKTHROUGH	EXTRUSION PRESSURE ($tonf/in^2$) INITIAL STEADY STATE	REMARKS ON STEADY STATE PRESSURE	PRODUCT FINISH
Titanium 130	Trilac 45	DTD.585	54	48	Oscillatory	Arrest marks
Titanium 130	Trilac 45	Glycerine 80% Ethylene Glycol 20%	52	48	Oscillatory	Arrest marks
Titanium 130	Trilac 45	Tellus 27	53	48	Constant	Good
Titanium 130	Trilac 45	Castor oil	52	48	Constant	Good
Titanium 130	None	Castor oil	69	48	Rising	Scored, poor
Titanium 130	Anodised	Castor oil	52	48	Rising	Fair
Titanium 130	Dry film graphite	Castor oil	52	48	Rising	Fair
Titanium 130	Graphite grease	Castor oil	52	48	Constant	Good
Copper	None	Castor oil	66	58	Constant	Good
Copper	None	Tellus 27	66	58	Constant	Good
Copper	None	DTD.585	67	58	Constant	Good
Copper	None	Glycerine 80% Ethylene Glycol 20%	66	58	Constant	Good
Copper	Trilac 45	Castor oil	70	58	Constant	Good
Copper	Graphite grease	Castor oil	74	58	Constant	Good

Table 4[35]

MATERIAL	VICKERS HARDNESS NO. (kg/mm^2)	NOMINAL COMPOSITION (per cent)	RANGE OF EXTRUSION RATIO R	EXTRUSION PRESSURE $p = a + b \ln R$	
				a ($tonf/in^2$)	b ($tonf/in^2$)
High conductivity copper	55	Cu 99·9 min	3 to 14	2·5	26
70/30 brass	70	Zn 30, Cu rem.	2 to 6	−13	50
12 % nickel silver	95	Zn 26, Ni 12, Cu rem.	2 to 6	0	47
99·5 % aluminium	19	Al 99·5 min	3 to 30	0	10
Aluminium Alloy HE15-W	84	Cu 4, Mg 0·85, Si 0·9 Fe 1, Mn 1·2, Al rem.	3 to 18	5	23
IMI Titanium 130	190	Ti	1·5 to 4·5	7·5	51
IMI Titanium 230	212	Cu 2, Ti rem.	1·5 to 4·0	10	51
IMI Titanium 205	260*	Mo 15, Ti rem.	1·2 to 2·2	22	48
IMI Titanium 205	300*	Mo 15, Ti rem.	1·2 to 2·2	18	60
IMI Titanium 314A	340	Al 4, Mn 4, Ti rem.	1·4 to 2·2	3	108
IMI Titanium 318A	340	Al 6, V4, Ti rem.	1·4 to 2·2	5	96
IMI Zirconium 20	180	Sn 1·5, Ni 0·5, Fe 0·1 Cr 0·1, Zr rem.	1·4 to 4·5	14	37
IMI Niobium alloy SU16	254	W 11, Mo 3, Hf 2, Nb rem.	1·4 to 2·7	12	76
Niobium-zirconium alloy	292	Zr 25, Nb rem.	1·4 to 2·8	18	74

* Hardness varied according to metallurgical heat-treatment.

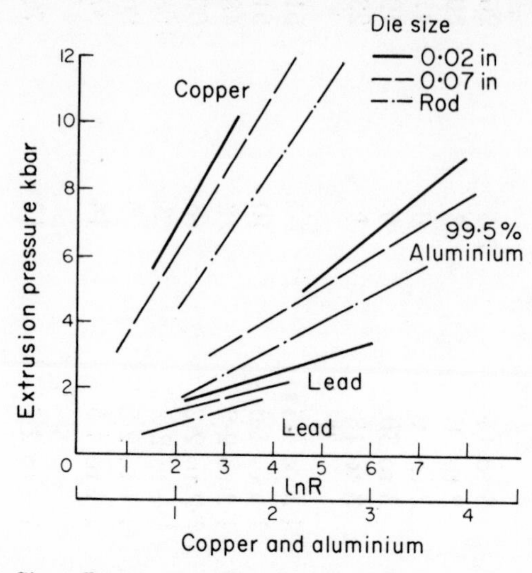

Fig. 85. Size effect on extrusion pressure. (*After Lowe* et al., *Ref. 35.*)

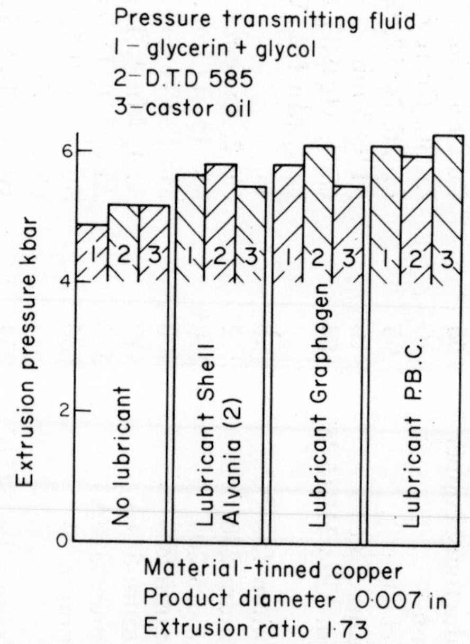

Fig. 86. Effects of pressure transmitting fluid and lubricants on pressure in wire extrusion. (*After Lowe* et al., *Ref. 34.*)

Copper wires down to 0·002 in diameter were extruded by Low *et al.*[34] and a significant size effect was observed. The pressure required for 0·002 in was about 50 % higher than for 0·25 in diameter at the same extrusion ratio. Similar size effects were found by Lowe *et al.*[35] for lead, aluminium and copper (Fig. 85). Experiments showed that the pressure transmitting fluids without additives are the most effective lubricants, if the wire diameter is less than 0·010 in, as illustrated in Fig. 86.[34]

Duffill and Mellor[44] made careful experiments in an attempt to separate the contribution of redundant work in both wire-drawing and hydrostatic extrusion. Their results indicate that the theories of both Pugh and Avitzur over-estimate the redundant work for large reductions and/or large die angles. They point out also the rather interesting fact that the expression for the main redundant work in these theories, viz. $[\alpha/\sin^2\alpha - \cot\alpha]$, differs from Siebel's well-known expression $[\frac{2}{3}\alpha]$ by less than 2 % for included die angles of less than 45°. Thus Siebel's expression could also suffer the same criticism, at least for large reductions. Their results are characterised by the behaviour illustrated in Fig. 87, from which it can be seen that for larger reductions the measured hydrostatic extrusion pressure is considerably less than that predicted theoretically. Although not stated by the authors, it is possible that the high strain rates (approximately 20 per second

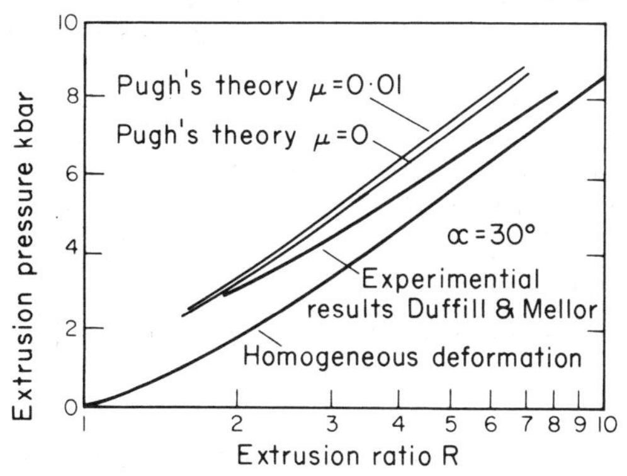

Fig. 87. Comparison of extrusion pressures for copper, 60° die. (*After Duffill* et al., *Ref. 44.*)

at the higher reductions) may have caused heating and consequent softening of the billet material, so that the room temperature stress/strain curve used to obtain the curve for homogeneous deformation would not be correct. This is purely conjecture, however; the authors in fact suggest that, if anything, the high strain rate would raise the flow stress of the material. Their experimental results, which are similar for mild steel and aluminium also, are at variance with those of Pugh, who obtained good agreement with this theory.

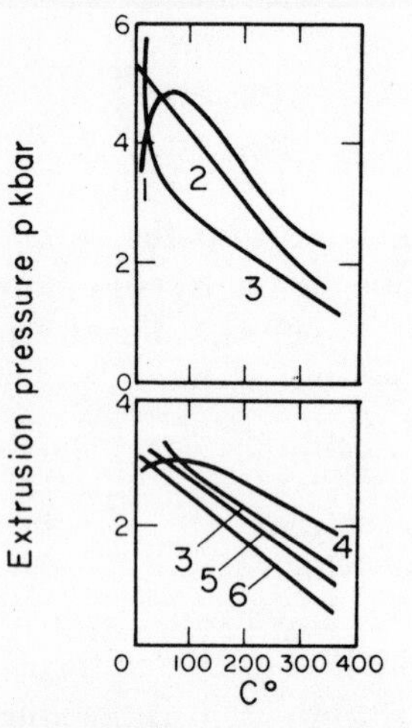

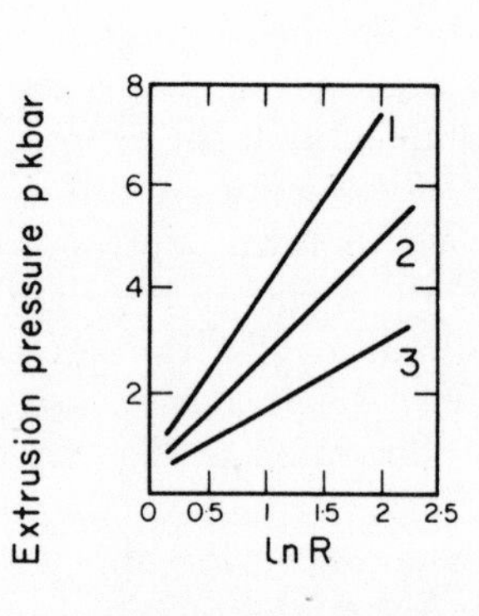

Commercially pure aluminium extruded at 72% reduction

1 transformer oil
2 kerosene + transformer oil (0·75 + 0·25)
3 kerosene + graphite (0·5+0·5)
4 solidol lubricating grease
5 graphite
6 solidol + graphite (0·5+0·5)

Commercially pure aluminium extruded by a mixture of kerosene + transformer oil (0·75+0·25)

1 20°C
2 150°C
3 300°C

Fig. 88. Hot hydrostatic extrusion of aluminium. (After Beresnev et al., *Ref. 17.)*

The process of hot hydrostatic extrusion seems to have been experimentally investigated for the first time by Beresnev *et al.*[17] The apparatus on which this work was carried out could accept pressures of 10 kb at temperatures up to 400°C; it was very similar to that illustrated in Fig. 71, the main addition being that the container was surrounded by a tubular furnace. Specimens of commercially pure aluminium were extruded at 72% area reduction using various fluids; the results are illustrated in Fig. 88. It was found that fluids could be divided into two groups, namely Group I, which increase extrusion pressure with heating, and Group II, which decrease extrusion pressure with heating. Some of the fluids in these groups are listed below:

Group I—fluids which increase extrusion pressure with heating: Solidol (a lubricating grease); hypoid gear grease; medium grade machine oil; transformer oil; vacuum oil.
Group II—fluids which decrease extrusion pressure with heating: Kerosene; ethyl alcohol; water; graphite.

The first group contains mineral oils with high boiling points which at one stage or another contain fatty acids. The reason for the worsening of the lubricating properties of these oils with increase in temperature is given as the loss of the property of the fatty acids to form and maintain a lubricating film at the interface when heated to a critical temperature. This hypothesis was tested by adding oleic acid to the kerosene-transformer oil mixture, the results presented in Fig. 89 clearly verify the hypothesis. Using mixtures of materials from Groups I and II, it was found that the extrusion pressure could be reduced below that for the pure substance alone, provided (in general) that more than 50% of the mixture was of the substance which reduces the pressure. The greatest reduction in extrusion pressure was observed with a mixture of graphite and lubricating grease in equal proportions (see Fig. 88, curve 6). These authors also measured the thickness of the fluid film surrounding the specimen, but it is not clear how this was determined. They quote the following figures, representing the film thickness in microns during steady-state hydrostatic extrusion:

Table 5

FLUID	FILM THICKNESS IN MICRONS ROOM TEMPERATURE	120°C
Mineral Oil	8–10	10–12
Kerosene, water, alcohol	3 – 4	5 – 7
Graphite	12	15

In their experiments, they recorded the pressure at the beginning of extrusion and estimated that the film thickness would be only $\frac{1}{2}$ to $\frac{1}{3}$ of the figures quoted above during this initial phase. From this they concluded that a mixed lubrication condition must precede full fluid lubrication in the steady state.

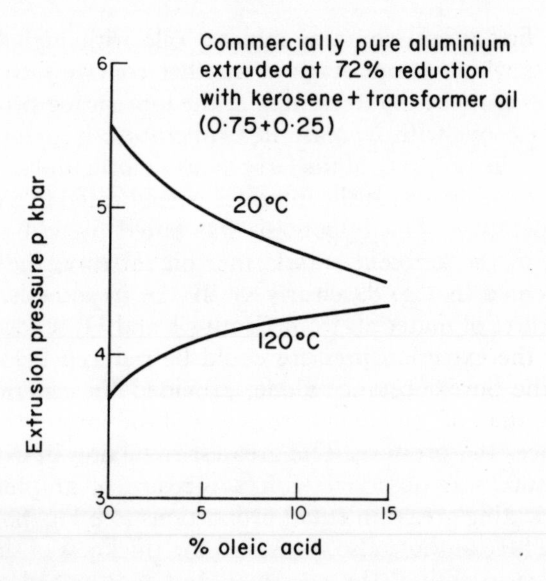

Fig. 89. Effect of oleic acid in hot hydrostatic extrusion. (*After Beresnev* et al., *Ref. 17.*)

5.2 EXTRUSION OF DIFFICULT MATERIALS AND COMPLEX SECTIONS

Hydrostatic extrusion offers particular advantages in forming difficult materials and complex sections, where existing methods are unsuccessful or expensive.

At the National Engineering Laboratory, annealed high speed steel was extruded by hydrostatic extrusion through a 45° die and a crack-free product obtained. The same material cracked in conventional extrusion through a 120° die, owing to the large shear strains in the billet material near the billet/die interface.

It has been known for some time that superimposed high fluid pressure increases the ductility of materials, i.e. under high pressure the strain at fracture is significantly larger than under atmospheric conditions.[4, 5, 23, 124–130] Consequently, large reductions can be achieved in extrusion, where compressive stresses predominate in the deformation zone, while instability and fracture limits the deformation to much smaller values in processes where tensile stresses are the determining factor, such as in wire or sheet drawing. However, in the cold extrusion of brittle materials the compressive stresses imposed by the die could be still insufficient to prevent fracture. In such cases the material is extruded into a pressurised fluid, the extrusion pressure being increased by the magnitude of the back pressure. This increases the hydrostatic component of stress in the deformation zone, which could be sufficient to prevent fracture.[128, 131] Since the extrusion pressure is different for various extrusion ratios, the back pressure that must be superimposed on a particular material to prevent fracture, varies with the extrusion ratio. For example, in the fluid-to-fluid extrusion of rolled molybdenum, the largest back pressure was needed at an extrusion ratio of 2, when the die pressure and the hydrostatic component of stress in the deformation zone was at a minimum.[5] As the extrusion pressure increases towards higher or lower extrusion ratios, the back pressure could be reduced and a crackfree product still obtained. Pugh and his co-workers and several other investigators carried out such experiments with a number of brittle materials, with similar results.

Fiorentino and his co-workers[136] have suggested that, in addition to the described role of backpressure in preventing fracture and possibly even healing up existing micro-voids in the deformation zone, back pressure also ensures a higher residual ductility of the material than extrusion without backpressure. This higher ductility allows the residual tensile stresses, which could otherwise cause fracture on the release of pressure, to be relieved by small plastic deformations. They showed the importance of residual surface stresses in causing fracture by extruding brittle materials through double reduction dies, the second reduction being very small so that the plastic flow was confined to layers near the surface. On exit from the second die, the outer fibres are axially compressed in the elastic manner by the core; thus, the residual surface tensile stresses are reduced or even residual compressive surface stresses are produced which prevent surface cracking. Beryllium, which fractured on extrusion from a standard die, remained crackfree on extrusion from a double reduction die of the same ratio. Work on hydrostatic extrusion using a double reduction die has also been carried out at Imperial College, London.[137]

Hydrostatic extrusion offers significant advantages in the production of complex sections. The main advantages are that, since the dies are supported by the pressurised fluid, complex die assemblies can be built up simply, from a number of components, many of which are re-usable for a number of different applications; furthermore, an abundant supply of fluid should ensure good lubrication.

A great variety of sections was produced in the early work of Pugh and his co-workers[5] and by Beresnev *et al.*[23] This included hexagonal, triangular, geared, twisted, etc., solid sections, composite billets and hollow sections, which are difficult or impossible to extrude conventionally. If round billets were extruded into sections, pressures were usually higher than those necessary for the extrusion of round billets into round rods. However, another advantage of hydrostatic extrusion—the fact that shaped billets can be used—is particularly useful in such cases. The billet shape can approximate the shape of the final product so that extrusion pressures can be kept to a minimum. For example, when a fluted section was extruded from round copper rod it required about 10 kbar pressure at an extrusion ratio of 3·6, while from a rectangular billet the extrusion ratio was only 2·6 and the pressure 7·2 kbar.[5]

This aspect of hydrostatic extrusion continues to attract a great deal of interest, and more recently several workers have made a systematic study of the subject.

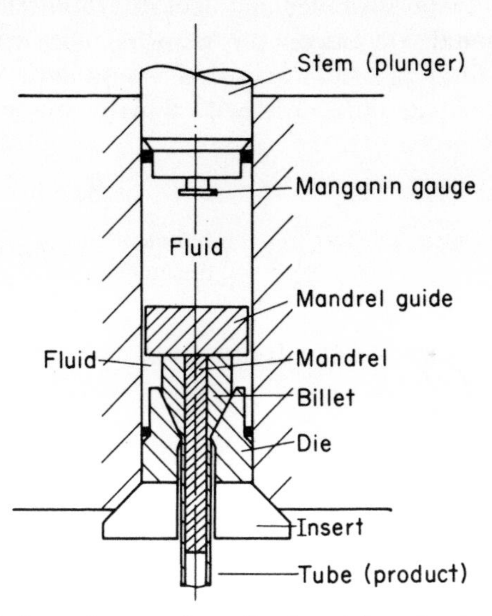

Fig. 90. Hydrostatic extrusion of tube with a floating mandrel. (After Fiorentino et al., *Ref. 121.)*

Fiorentino *et al.*[121] extruded tubes, using a floating mandrel arrangement as illustrated in Fig. 90. (A fixed mandrel arrangement would have the mandrel and mandrel guide in a fixed position, supported on a hollow cylinder resting on top of the die as shown in Fig. 5.) An important feature of the floating mandrel system is that the mandrel cross-sectional area is unsupported; the billet end face thus carries an extra pressure equal to pA_m/A_b, where p is the fluid pressure, A_m is the cross-sectional area of the mandrel and A_b is the cross-sectional area of the billet. Thus, this system automatically gives billet augmentation, and lower fluid pressures are required than for solid rods.

The results of this research work are illustrated in Fig. 91, from which it can be seen that the billet end pressure (for the tubular products) is higher than the fluid pressure required for solid rods, due to the effect of friction on the mandrel, so that the advantage of billet augmentation is somewhat offset. In the case of a fixed mandrel system, there would be no billet augmentation and there would be additional friction on the mandrel above the die so that the fluid pressures required would be even higher than the billet end pressures needed in the floating mandrel system.

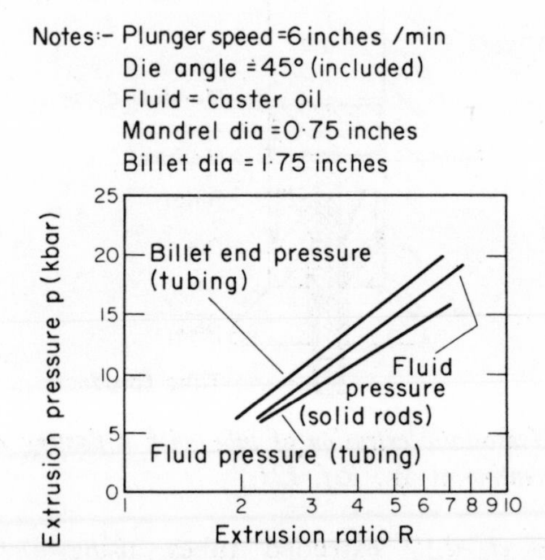

Fig. 91. Extrusion pressure in the extrusion of rod and tube with a floating mandrel. (*After Fiorentino* et al., *Ref. 121.*)

In the experimental study of the orthodox hydrostatic extrusion of sections, Thompson[62] extruded commercial purity aluminium through conical and flat-faced dies

(Fig. 92). The die land was about 0·015 in in all cases. In the flat-faced die the sealing block served to provide a seal between the die assembly and the billet. In some cases, it was found necessary to machine a groove into the front face of the die plate to maintain this seal.

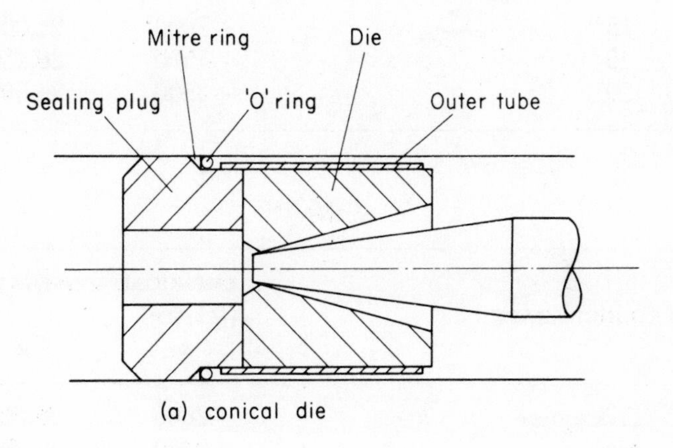

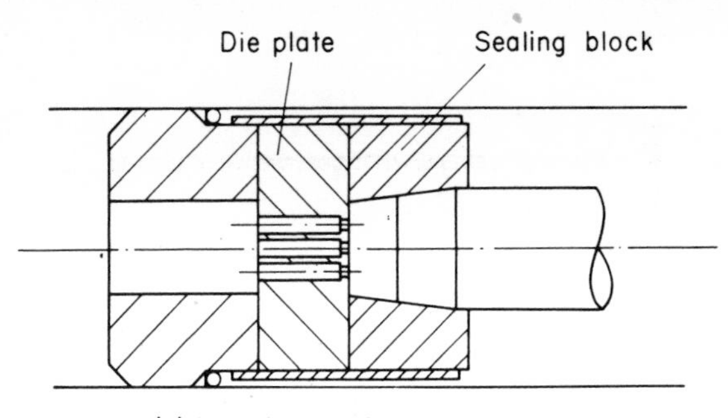

Fig. 92. Conical and flat-faced die assemblies. (After Thompson, Ref. 62.)

In extrusion through conical dies, the billet nose angle was always slightly less than the die angle, to eliminate the initial pressure peak. The empirical constants of equation (10*a*) for round-to-round extrusion are shown in Table 6 and for round-to-section extrusion through 30° dies in Table 7.

Table 6[62]

INCLUDED DIE ANGLE	EMPIRICAL CONSTANTS (lbf/in²)	
	a	*b*
15°	−7000	26,000
45°	−3500	26,250
90°	+2500	26,600

Table 7[62]

PRODUCT SHAPE	EMPIRICAL CONSTANTS (lbf/in²)	
	a	*b*
Triangular	+2000	26,000
Square	+2000	26,300
Hexagonal	+4000	26,800

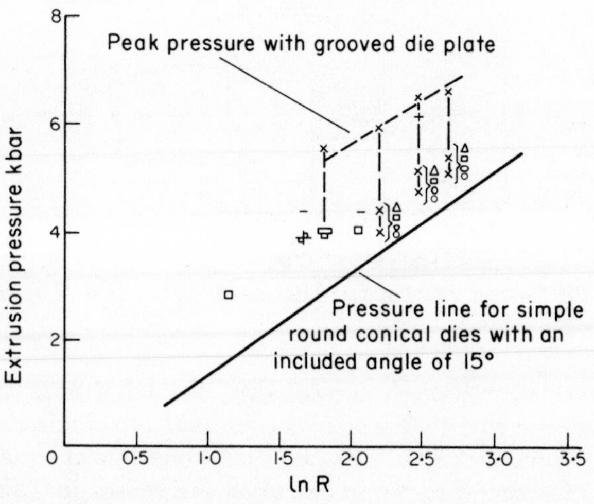

Fig. 93. Extrusion of complex sections through flat-faced dies. (After Thompson, Ref. 62.)

With flat-faced dies, a dead metal zone formed which became detached from the rest of the billet on removal from the die. Successful extrusions were also carried out when the sealing ring was replaced by an annular guide bush having a parallel bore. Some of the results obtained in this manner are shown in Fig. 93.

Finally, round billets were extruded into wire through flat-faced multi-hole dies, with all extrusions of the same cross-sectional area. For a sealing block of 15° included angle the results are shown in Fig. 94, where the effective extrusion ratio is

$$R_{\text{eff}} = \frac{\text{cross-sectional area of billet}}{\text{cross-sectional area of a single extrusion.}}$$

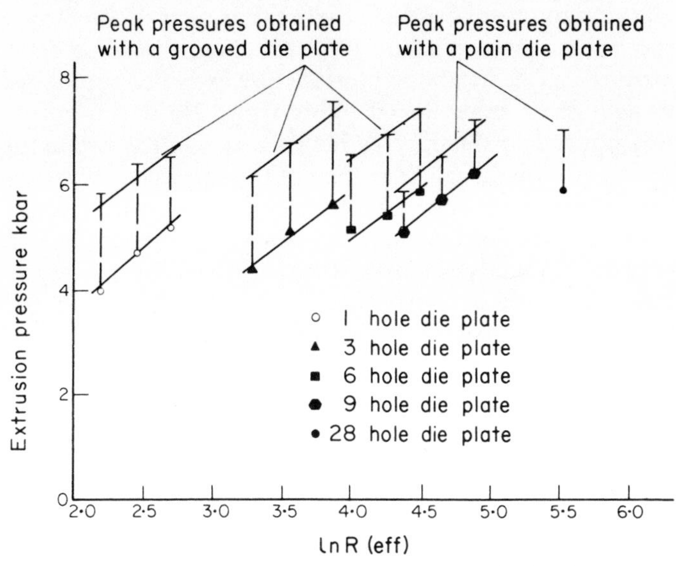

Fig. 94. Extrusion of wire through multi-hole flat-faced dies. (After Thompson, Ref. 62.)

5.3 PROPERTIES OF THE PRODUCT

Using product augmentation, Bridgman[4] converted commercial wire of 0·076 in. diameter into wire 0·026 in.

diameter in six passes. For the same reduction, fifteen passes were necessary at atmospheric pressure. Up to a strain of 1·3 the properties of the wire produced by the two methods were indistinguishable. Beyond 1·3 the properties of the drawn wire deteriorated until at 1·9 the residual ductility was zero and the tensile strength and true fracture stress coincided at 430,000 lbf/in^2. On the other hand, the wire drawn under pressure showed no comparable deterioration: at a strain of 1·9 the residual ductility was 0·29, the tensile strength 530,000 lbf/in^2 and the true fracture stress 720,000 lbf/in^2.

Beresnev *et al.* annealed commercially pure aluminium and copper specimens, then hydrostatically extruded one batch and drew another.[20] It was found that after 90% reduction the U.T.S. of the hydrostatically extruded aluminium was about 50% higher than that of the drawn specimens. Copper, after 70% reduction, showed a 20% greater U.T.S. for the hydrostatically extruded specimens as against those produced by drawing. No improvement was noticed in ductility as between specimens produced by the two methods. Annealing of the specimens revealed that those hydrostatically extruded were still stronger after recrystallisation than the drawn specimens. It was concluded that hydrostatic extrusion either suppresses the formation and development of submicro defects of the crack type or creates a higher density of dislocations with a more favourable distribution throughout the volume of the material.

This research was later backed up by further work[21, 22] in which it was shown that hydrostatic pressure on its own was not sufficient to eliminate defects of the pore and crack type in a metal. When accompanied by sufficient plastic deformation, however, hydrostatic pressure appears to be able to eliminate such defects. Specimens of industrial grade copper were subjected to creep extensions from 16 to 20% by subjecting them to stresses of 5–6 kg/mm^2 for 100 h at 400°C. This produced pores and cracks along grain boundaries, quite visible under the microscope. Smaller specimens were produced from these for subsequent plastic deformation under pressure. Initially, specimens were subjected to 100 kb without attempting to apply simultaneous plastic deformation. As a result, there was some plastic deformation (2-5 %) but this did not alter the overall picture; the structural defects were retained on the grain boundaries. On the other hand, specimens subjected to tension under high hydrostatic pressure revealed no defects in the narrow part of the neck (for pressures above 4 kbar). The explanation was put forward that plastic deformation creates ridges between the walls of the pores bringing them together to within atomic distances, thus permitting diffusion processes to occur with a consequent 'growing together' of the pore surfaces. This becomes more vigorous as the pressure and deformation are increased. The ductility rises, and the defects eventually become insignificant as regards reducing the strength of the material.

Hydrostatic extrusion of copper specimens deliberately produced with pores and grain boundary defects showed the same effects. The strength and ductility of hydrostatically extruded specimens with defects was higher than those deformed by wire drawing to the same extent. Careful measurement of the density of these specimens showed that hydrostatic extrusion restored the density (closed the defects) approximately 2–3 times faster than did wire drawing. Parallel experiments on defect-free copper

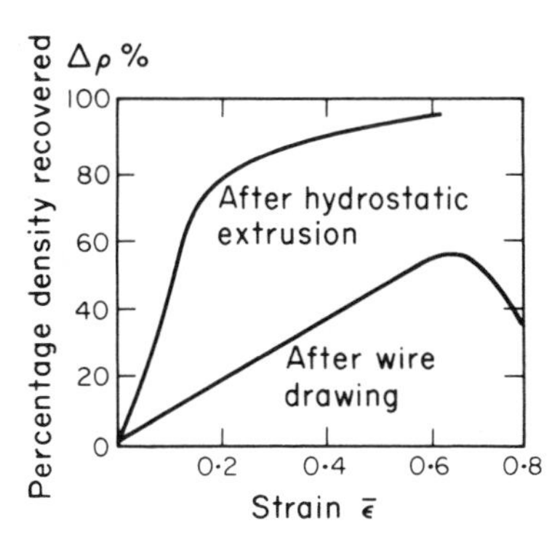

Fig. 95. Density recovery of copper with defects. (*After Beresnev* et al., *Ref. 22.*)

revealed that, whilst hydrostatic extrusion did not affect the density significantly, wire-drawing reduced the density (introduced defects) as reduction increased. These effects, illustrated in Figs. 95 and 96, were discussed further in a paper by Martynov *et al*[129], by Herø *et al.*[50] for a range of aluminium alloys and by Rozner *et al.*[123] for two intermetallic compounds. The relation between the ultimate tensile strength and elongation of cold drawn and hydrostatically extruded TiNi intermetallic compound is shown in Fig. 97.

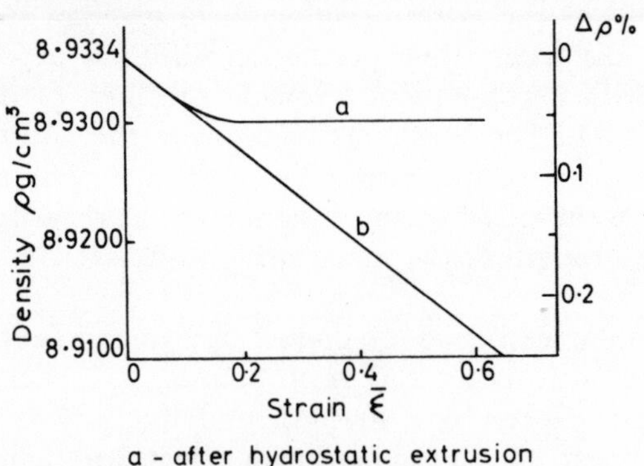

Fig. 96. Effect of deformation on the density of defect-free copper. (After Beresnev et al., *Ref. 22.)*

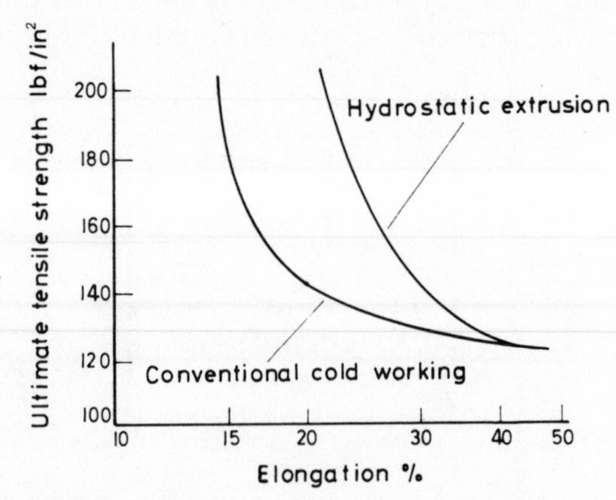

Fig. 97. Relation between U.T.S. and elongation for cold worked TiNi. (After Rozner et al., *Ref. 123.)*

All these results have been obtained at relatively low extrusion ratios, when the ultimate tensile strength and proof stress increased, while elongation and reduction in area decreased, a work-hardening effect very similar to that found in conventional extrusion.[15] Hardness gradients, with hardness gradually increasing towards the surface, were reported to exist across the cross-sections of specimens produced by hydrostatic extrusion, particularly at die angles other than the optimum angle at which extrusion pressure is at a minimum. This gradient was said to be substantially less than in conventional extrusion. In the latter the large increase in hardness from the centre towards the surface (Fig. 98) was explained as being due to non-homogeneous deformation, whereas in hydrostatic

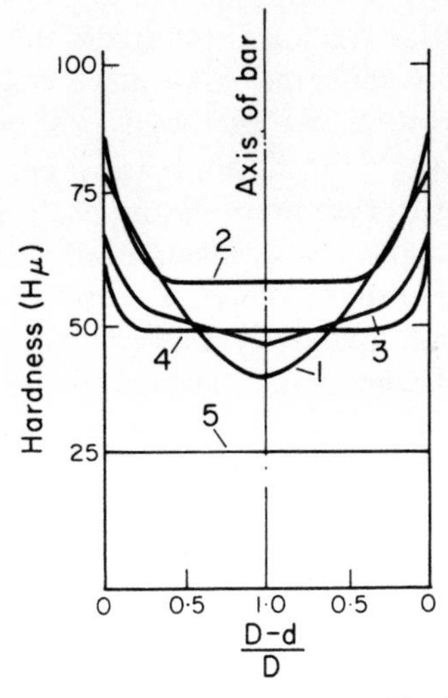

1 Conventional extrusion, 45° die angle
2 Hydrostatic extrusion, 10° die angle
3 Hydrostatic extrusion, 120° die angle
4 Hydrostatic extrusion, 45° die angle
5 Annealed material
D Initial diameter of billet
d Diameter of extrusion

Fig. 98. Hardness distribution in conventionally and hydrostatically extruded copper at R = 2. (After Beresnev et al., *Ref. 15.)*

extrusion the homogeneity is improved because shearing of the material along the die face is reduced as a consequence of the good lubrication and low friction effects. The deformation pattern becomes almost uniform across the section at the optimum die angle; therefore, the hardness gradients become very small. Subsequent investigations offered no conclusive evidence that so great a difference in patterns of hardness distribution exists in specimens produced by conventional extrusion on the one hand and at various die angles in orthodox hydrostatic extrusion on the other. In fact, for small extrusion ratios and 180° die angle, a considerably more uniform hardness distribution was reported for conventionally extruded 99·5% aluminium billets than that shown in Fig. 98 for a 45° die when, owing to the less uniform deformation, exactly the opposite would be expected. For large extrusion ratios the hardness across the section was shown to be almost uniform.[132] No proof could be found that, in the hydrostatically extruded product, hardness distribution depends on the die angle and it becomes almost uniform only at the optimum die angle.[61] In fact, the distribution of hardness was substantially uniform over the cross-section of both conventionally and hydrostatically extruded specimens, and only marginal differences between them were found in the mean hardness values.

The beneficial effect of hydrostatic extrusion in the closing-up of pores and cavities promises to be attractive for the production of powder-compacted articles. In experiments reported by Johnsson,[120] isostatically compacted billets of aluminium powder were hydrostatically extruded satisfactorily at extrusion ratios greater than approximately 5·5 : 1. It was possible to produce satisfactory (uncracked) products at lower extrusion ratios by fluid-to-fluid extrusion, the back-pressure being necessary to prevent fracture occurring as extrusion ratio decreased.

The effect of heat generated during hydrostatic extrusion, the consequent temperature rise and change in mechanical properties has received attention.[50, 61, 62, 122] The incremental temperature rise during plastic deformation in an element of material in time Δt can be written in the form

$$\Delta T = \frac{\beta}{Jc\rho}\,\sigma\,\Delta\varepsilon = \frac{\beta}{Jc\rho}\,\sigma\,\dot{\varepsilon}\,\Delta t \qquad (71)$$

where σ is the instantaneous effective yield stress of the element of material, $\Delta\varepsilon$ is the local effective strain increment, $\dot{\varepsilon}$ is the local effective strain rate, ρ is density, c specific heat, J is the mechanical equivalent of heat and β is the proportion of the deformation energy converted into heat, about 90%.[133] The yield stress of the material is a function of strain, strain rate and temperature

$$\sigma = F(\varepsilon, \dot{\varepsilon}, T) \qquad (72)$$

Some of this heat is conducted away by the tool, some increases the temperature of the material not yet worked, i.e. conducted back in the billet, and some remains in the shaped material to be lost subsequently by conduction and radiation to the environment. The heat conducted to the undeformed billet and the temperature rise in the deformation zone itself could reduce the yield stress of the material; this could be due to the temperature dependence of the yield stress and/or the recovery and recrystallisation of the deforming material. The heat retained by the shaped product could result in further recovery and recrystallisation, since both these processes are time dependent. Furthermore, because the rate of these metallurgical processes increases with strain and temperature, at large strains and strain rates the effects of work hardening and thermal softening could be in equilibrium; plastic deformation would then bring no significant change in material properties, i.e. the work hardening effects usually associated with plastic strains could be reduced or may be completely absent.

The significance of thermal effects in orthodox hydrostatic extrusion at larger ratios has been demonstrated.[61] For copper at an extrusion ratio of 16 and 120° die angle ($\varepsilon_3 = 3{\cdot}53$, equ. 6), the mean hardness and 0·1% proof stress was almost the same as for the annealed material (Fig. 15). Reduction in area and elongation values showed a corresponding increase at large extrusion ratios (Fig. 99). Similar results were obtained for aluminium.[50, 62, 122]

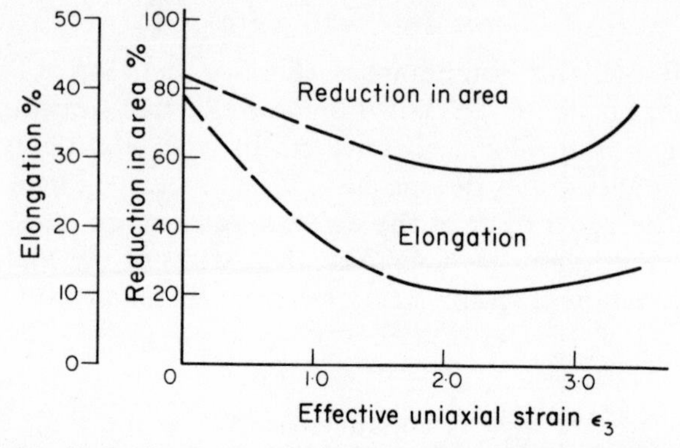

Fig. 99. Reduction in area and elongation of hydrostatically extruded copper. (After Lengyel et al., *Ref. 61.)*

The dimensional accuracy of the products, extruded under steady state conditions, is good, as illustrated in Fig. 100.[119] The diameter of 10 mm bars varied by less than 10 μm, and this is attributed to the die having external fluid support which varies with the billet/die interface pressure, thus maintaining the changes in the die diameter during extrusion at a low value. The surface of products has a matt finish but, if lubrication conditions are favourable, the surface texture is reasonably good.[119]

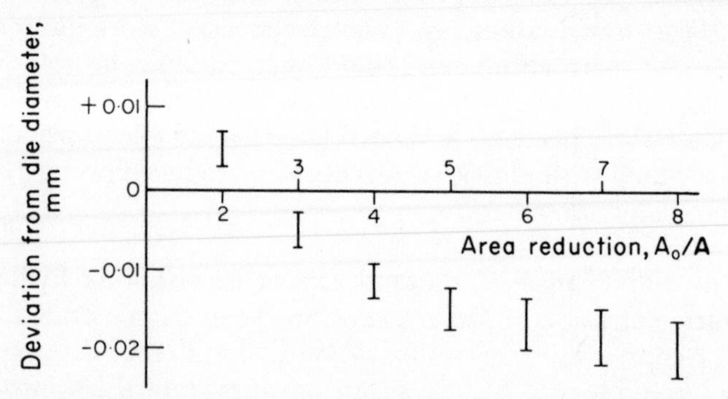

Fig. 100. Deviation of product diameter from die diameter. (After Johnsson, Ref. 119.)

References

1. British Complete Specification No. 19356, 1893. "Improvements in the Manufacture of Metal Tubes, tubular and hollow articles, plates, rods, bars, wires, and the like, and in means and apparatus therefor", by J. Robertson.
2. W. Johnson. Introductory address, Conference on High Pressure Engineering, 11th to 15th September 1967, *Proc. Instn Mech. Engrs*, **182,** Part 3C, ix (1967–8).
3. H. Kronberger. "Hydrostatic extrusion". *Proc. Roy. Soc.*, A**331,** 331–47 (1969).
4. P. W. Bridgman. *Studies in large plastic flow and fracture*, McGraw Hill, 1952, pp. 177–9.
5. H. Ll. D. Pugh."Recent developments in Cold Forming". Bulleid Memorial Lectures, 1965, Vol. IIIB, Lecture 3, 1965. University of Nottingham.
6. H. Ll. D. Pugh. "Pressurized extrusion". British Patent Applications 17603, 1958; 6626, 1959; 20500, 1961.
7. H. Ll. D.Pugh. "The mechanical properties and deformation characteristics of metals and alloys under pressure". ASTM Int. Conf. on Materials, Philadelphia, February 1964.
8. H. Ll. D. Pugh and K. Ashcroft. "Hydrostatic (ramless) extrusion of metals by liquid pressure". Symp. on the physics and chemistry of high pressure, 163–76. London Soc. of Chemical Industries, 1962.
9. H. Ll. D. Pugh, J. Lees, K. Ashcroft and D. A. Gunn, "High Pressure Research at the National Engineering Laboratory". *The Engineer*, **212** (5508), 258 (1961).
10. H. Ll. D. Pugh. "The redundant work and friction in the hydrostatic extrusion of pure aluminium and an aluminium alloy". *J. Mech. Eng. Sci.*, **6** (4), 362 (1964).
11. H. Ll. D. Pugh and A. H. Low. "The hydrostatic extrusion of difficult metals". *J. Inst. Metals*, **93,** 201 (1964–5).
12. H. Ll. D. Pugh and D. Green. "The effect of hydrostatic pressure on the plastic flow and fracture of metals". *Proc. I. Mech. E.*, **179** (1) (1964–5).
13. H. Ll. D. Pugh. "Extruding unheated metal with high-pressure fluid". *New Scientist*, No. 333 (4th April 1963).
14. B. I. Beresnev, L. F. Vereshchagin and Y. N. Ryabinin. "Characteristics of the rheological behaviour of metals extruded under hydrostatic pressure". *Izvest. Akad. Nauk, O.T.N.*, **5,** 48–55 (1957).

15. B. I. Beresnev, L. F. Vereshchagin and Yu. N. Ryabinin. "The variation in the mechanical properties of non-ferrous metals and alloys on hydraulically extruding them at high pressure". *Fiz. Metal. Metalloved*, **7,** No. 7, 247–253 (1959).
16. B. I. Beresnev, L. F. Vereshchagin and Yu. N. Ryabinin. "Extrusion of metals by means of a liquid under high pressure". *Izv. Akad. Nauk, S.S.S.R.; Mekhi Mashin*, **7,** 128 (1959).
17. B. I. Beresnev, D. K. Bulychev and K. P. Rodionov. "Features of the process of extruding metals with high pressure liquid at elevated temperatures". *Fiz. Metal. Metalloved*, **11,** No. 1, 115–21 (1961).
18. Yu. N. Riabinin, B. I. Beresnev and B. P. Demyashkevich, "Variation in the mechanical properties of iron deformed by high pressure hydro-extrusion". *Ibid.*, **11,** 630 (1961).
19. D. K. Bulychev and B. I. Beresnev. "Extrusion of iron by a high pressure liquid". *Ibid.*, **13,** No. 6, 942–4 (1962).
20. B. I. Beresnev and D. K. Bulychev. "Mechanical properties of hydro-extruded aluminium and copper". *Ibid.*, 16, No. 1, 117–23 (1963).
21. B. I. Beresnev, L. F. Vereshchagin and Yu. N. Riabinin. "Conditions of extrusion and variation of the mechanical properties of metal in their extrusion by a high-pressure fluid". *Inzh-fiz. Zh.*, **3,** 43 (1963).
22. B. I. Beresnev, D. K. Bulychev, M. G. Gaydukov, Ye. D. Martynov, K. P. Rodionov and Yu. N. Ryabinin. "Closing of pores and cracks in copper due to high-pressure hydro-extrusion". *Fiz. Metal Metalloved*, **18,** No. 5, 778–83 (1964).
23. B. I. Beresnev, L. P. Vereshchagin, Yu. N. Riabinin and L. D. Livshits. *Some problems of large plastic deformation of metals at high pressures*. Pergamon Press Ltd., 1963. Russian original published by the USSR Academy of Sciences in 1960.
24. R. N. Randall, D. M. Davies, J. M. Sievgiej and P. Lowestein. "Experimental hydrostatic extrusion points to new production techniques". *Modern Metals*, **17** (7), 68 (1962).
25. R. J. Fiorentino, A. M. Sabroff and F. W. Boulger. "Hydrostatic extrusion of metals at Battelle". *Machinery Lloyd* (European Edit.), 17, 18 (1963).

26. Anon. Pressure Technology Corporation of America Progress Report 1964 (1) on Navy Bureau of Naval Weapons Contract NOW 64-D180-C.
27. A. Rozner and J. H. Faupel. "Some considerations of the mechanics of hydrostatic extrusion". *J. Franklin Institute*, **277** (3), 217 (1964).
28. D. Green. "An experimental high speed machine for the practical exploitation of hydrostatic extrusion". *J. Inst. Metals*, **93** (3), 65 (1964–5).
29. J. M. Alexander and B. Lengyel. "Semi-continuous hydrostatic extrusion of wire". *Proc. I. Mech. E.*, **180** (Part 31), 317 (1965–6).
30. B. Lengyel, D. J. Burns and L. V. Prasad. "Design of containers for a semi-continuous hydrostatic extrusion production machine". *Proc. 7th International M.T.D.R. Conference, 1966*. Pergamon.
31. B. Lengyel. "A semi-continuous hydrostatic extrusion production process". *Metals and Materials*, January 1968.
32. B. Lengyel and P. G. Ashford. "An experimental pre-production unit for semi-continuous hydrostatic extrusion". *Proc. 8th Int. M.T.D.R. Conference, 1967*. Pergamon.
33. J. Crawley, J. A. Pennell and A. Saunders. "Some problems in the design and development of hydrostatic extrusion systems". Conference on High Pressure Engineering 11th to 15th September 1967, *Proc. I. Mech. E.*, **182,** Part 3C, 180 (Paper 23), (1967–8).
34. A. H. Low, C. J. Donaldson and P. T. Wilkinson. "Developments in hydrostatic extrusion at the National Engineering Laboratory". *Ibid.*, 188 (Paper 22), and 340 (Discussion).
35. B. W. H. Lowe and D. Goold. "An account of some recent experimental work on the hydrostatic extrusion of non-ferrous metals". *Ibid.*, 197 (Paper 10) and 341 (Discussion).
36. B. Lengyel and J. M. Alexander. "Design of a production machine for semi-continuous hydrostatic extrusion". *Ibid.*, 217 (Paper 9), 342 (Discussion).
37. H. K. Slater and D. Green. "Augmented hydrostatic extrusion of continuous bar". *Ibid.*, 217 (Paper 14), 343 (Discussion).
38. W. Johnson and F. W. Travis. "A tool for explosive hydrodynamic extrusion". *Ibid.*, 223 (Paper 2), 344 (Discussion).

39. F. W. Travis and W. Johnson. "Explosive hydrodynamic extrusion pressures generated and other phenomena". *Ibid.*, 231 (Paper 1), 344 (Discussion).
40. D. H. Newhall and L. H. Abbott. "A contemporary version of the Bridgman-Birch 30 kb apparatus and certain ancillary devices". *Ibid.*, 288 (Paper 32).
41. A. W. Duffill and P. B. Mellor. "A comparison between the conventional and hydrostatic methods of cold extrusion through conical dies". C.I.R.P. Conference, September 1968.
42. H. S. R. Iyengar and W. B. Rice. "Lubrication on hydrostatic extrusion". C.I.R.P. Conference, September 1968.
43. P. J. Thompson. "Hydrostatic extrusion of steel". MS. No. 5, *Proc. 9th Int. M.T.D.R. Conference*, Pergamon (1968).
44. A. W. Duffill and P. B. Mellor. "A comparison of wire-drawing and hydrostatic extrusion through straight conical dies". *Ibid.*, MS. No. 3.
45. B. Parsons, D. Bretherton and B. N. Cole. "A preliminary investigation of the combined hydrostatic extrusion and drawing processes". *Ibid.*, MS. No. 3.
46. A. W. Duffill, C. J. Hooke and P. B. Mellor. "Design of straight conical dies for hydrostatic extrusion". *Ibid.*, MS. No. 44.
47. R. J. Pick, D. J. Burns and B. Lengyel. "Computer design of elastic multi-component cylindrical pressure vessels subjected to cyclic internal pressure". *Ibid.*, MS. No. 31.
48. D. C. Harvey and B. Lengyel. "Pressure vessels under cyclic loading: test rig and initial results". *Ibid.*, MS. No. 35.
49. E. R. Lambert and S. Kobayashi. "An approximate solution for the mechanics of axisymmetric extrusion". *Ibid.*, MS. No. 9.
50. H. Herø and J. A. Mikkelsen. "Some mechanical and structural properties of hydrostatically extruded aluminium alloys". *J. Inst. Metals*, **97,** 18 (1969).
51. A. M. Sabroff and R. J. Fiorentino. Discussion, Conference on High Pressure Engineering 11th to 15th September 1967. *Proc. I. Mech. E.*, **182** (Part 3C), 328 (1967–8).
52. A. W. Duffill, P. B. Mellor and S. A. Tobias. "The design and development of a hydrostatic extrusion machine". *Int. J. Mach. Tool Res.*, **8,** 125 (1968).

53. J. M. Alexander and B. Lengyel. British Complete Specifications Nos. 12326/65, No. 56241/66 and No. 41249/67.
54. C. Sauve. "Lubrication problems in the extrusion process". *J. Inst. Metals*, **93,** 553–81 (1965).
55. E. Siebel. "The present state of knowledge of the mechanics of wire drawing" (in German). *Stahl u. Eisen*, 66/67 (11–22), 171–80 (1947).
56. R. Hill. *The mathematical theory of plasticity*, O.U.P., 1950.
57. W. Prager and P. G. Hodge, Jnr. *Theory of perfectly plastic solids*. J. Wiley, 1951.
58. B. Avitzur. "Hydrostatic extrusion". Paper No. 64-WA. PROD-20. *Trans. A.S.M.E.*
59. D. Hoffman and G. Sachs. *Introduction to the theory of plasticity*, 163–86, McGraw-Hill, New York, 1963.
60. M. J. Hillier. "A hydrodynamic model of hydrostatic extrusion". *Int. J. Production Research*, **5** (2), 171, (1966).
61. B. Lengyel and L. E. Culver. "Properties of materials extruded by orthodox hydrostatic extrusion". *J. Inst. Metals*, **97,** 97–103 (1969).
62. P. J. Thompson. "The hydrostatic extrusion of commercially pure aluminium solid sections". *J. Inst. Metals*, **96,** 257 (1968).
63. E. R. Lambert and S. Kobayashi. "A theory on the mechanics of axisymmetric extrusion through conical dies". *Mech. Eng. Science*, **10** (5), 367 (1968).
64. H. Ll. D. Pugh. "The cold extrusion of metals by a high pressure liquid". 1963 International Research in Production Engineering, A.S.M.E., p. 394.
65. O. Richmond and M. L. Devenpeck. "A die profile for maximum efficiency in strip drawing". *Proc. 4th U.S. Nat. Cong. Appl. Mech.*, **2,** 1053 (1962).
66. H. C. Sortais and S. Kobayashi. "An optimum die profile for axisymmetric extrusion". *Int. J. Mach. Tool Des. Res.*, **8,** 61 (1968).
67. H. Ford, *Advanced mechanics of materials*. Longmans, 1963.
68. A. Nadai, *Plasticity*. McGraw-Hill, 1931.
69. W. R. D. Manning, "High pressure engineering". Bulleid Memorial Lectures, University of Nottingham, 1962.
70. G. J. Franklin and J. L. M. Morrison, "Autofrettage of cylinders: prediction of pressure/external expansion curves and calculation of residual stresses". *Proc. Instn Mech. Engrs*, **174** (35), 947–74 (1960).

71. B. Crossland and D. J. Burns. "Behaviour of compound steel cylinders subjected to internal pressure". *Proc. Instn Mech. Engrs*, **175,** 1083 (1961).
72. H. Ll. D. Pugh "Recent developments in cold forming". Bulleid Memorial Lectures, Nottingham University, 1965. Vol. III.A, Lecture 1.
73. J. Case. *The strength of materials*. Edward Arnold & Co., 1925.
74. P. W. Bridgman. "Polymorphic transitions of 35 substances to 50,000 kg/cm^2". *Proc. Am. Acad. Arts Sci.*, **72,** 45–136 (1937).
75. P. W. Bridgman. "Some results in the field of high pressure physics". *Endeavour*, **10,** 63–9 (1951).
76. J. L. M. Morrison, B. Crossland and J. S. C. Parry. "Fatigue under triaxial stress: development of a testing machine and preliminary results". *Proc. Instn Mech. Engrs*, **170,** 21, 697–712 (1956).
77. J. L. M. Morrison, B. Crossland and J. S. C. Parry. "Strength of thick cylinders subjected to repeated internal pressure". *Proc. Instn Mech. Engrs*, **174,** 2, 65–114 (1960).
78. J. S. C. Parry. "Further results of fatigue under triaxial stress". *Proc. Int. Conf. of Fatigue of Metals* (*Inst. Mech. Eng.*), 132–7 (1956).
79. J. J. Blass and W. N. Findley. "The influence of the intermediate principal stress on fatigue under triaxial stresses". *Materials Res. & Standards*, **7,** 6, 254–61 (1967).
80. B. Crossland. "Effect of large hydrostatic pressures on the torsional fatigue strength of an alloy steel". *Proc. Int. Conf. on Fatigue of Metals* (*Inst. Mech. Eng.*), 138–49 (1956).
81. D. J. Burns and J. S. C. Parry. "Effect of large hydrostatic pressures on the torsional fatigue strength of two steels". *J. Mech. Eng. Sci.*, **6,** 3, 293–305 (1964).
82. B. A. Austin and B. Crossland. "Low endurance fatigue strength of thick-walled cylinders: development of a testing machine and preliminary results". *Proc. Instn Mech. Engrs*, **180,** 1A (1965–6).
83. J. S. C. Parry. "Fatigue of thick cylinders: further practical information". *Proc. Instn Mech. Engrs*, **180,** 1 (1965–1966).
84. T. E. Davidson, R. Eisenstadt and A. N. Reiner. "Fatigue characteristics of open-ended thick-walled cylinders under cyclic internal pressure". *J. Basic Eng. Trans. Amer. Soc. Mech. Eng.*, **85,** (D) 555 (1963).

85. D. J. Burns and J. S. C. Parry. "Effect of mean stress on the fatigue behaviour of thick-walled cylinders". *Proc. Instn Mech. Engrs,* **182** (3C), 72–80 (1967–8).
86. J. C. Gerdeen and R. J. Fiorentino. "Analysis of several high pressure container concepts". *Proc. Instn Mech. Engrs,* **182,** 3C, 1–10 (1967–8).
87. H. Kudo and S. Matsubara. *Stress analysis in cylindrical dies of finite length subjected to a band of internal pressure.* The Government Mechanical Laboratory, Tokyo, Japan.
88. P. W. Bridgman. *The physics of high pressure.* Bell and Sons, 1931.
89. V. A. Mikhaev. "Seals for very high hydraulic pressures". *Russian Eng. J.,* Vol XLVII, No. 4, p. 26.
90. A. Zeitlin and J. Brayman. "Ultra-high pressure calibration: influence of cubic workpiece configuration". In *High pressure measurement,* Butterworths, 1963, p. 301.
91. D. Green. "An automatic 1600 tons hydrostatic extrusion press". Lecture given at the Post-Experience Course on Hydrostatic Extrusion at Imperial College, July 1969.
92. M. S. Paterson. "O-ring seals for high pressure". *J. Sci. Instrum.,* **39,** 173 (1962).
93. W. B. Daniels and A. A. Hruschka. "Seals for pressures up to 10,000 atmospheres". *Review of Sci. Instrum.,* **28,** No. 12, 1058.
94. H. H. Buchter. *Apparate und Armaturen der chemischen Hochdrucktechnik,* Springer-Verlag, 1967.
95. H. Ll. D. Pugh. "An intermittent (semi-continuous) hydrostatic extrusion machine", NEL Report No. 344, February 1968.
96. D. G. Christopherson and H. Naylor. "Promotion of fluid lubrication in wire drawing". *Proc. Instn Mech. Engrs,* **169,** 643 (1955).
97. H. S. Cheng. "Plastohydrodynamic lubrication". "Friction and lubrication in metal processing", ASME, 1966.
98. J. G. Wistreich. "Lubrication in wire drawing". *Proc. Conf. Lubrication and Wear: Inst. Mech. Engrs.,* 505–11 (1957).
99. F. C. Bowden and D. Tabor. *Friction and lubrication.* Methuen and Co., 1956.
100. P. R. Lancaster and G. W. Rowe. "Experimental study of the influence of lubrication upon cold drawing under approximately plane-strain conditions". *Proc. Instn Mech. Engrs,* **178,** 69–88 (1964).

101. V. Evans and B. Avitzur. "Measurement of friction in drawing, extrusion and rolling". *Trans. ASME,* **90,** Series F (1), 72–80 (1968).
102. ASME Research Committee on Lubrication. *Viscosity and density of over 40 lubricating fluids* (1953).
103. P. W. Bridgman. "Further rough compression to 40,000 kg/cm^2, especially certain liquids". *Proc. Am. Acad. Arts Sci.,* **77,** 129–46 (1949).
104. P. S. Y. Chu and A. Cameron. "Compressibility and thermal expansion of oils". *J. Inst. Petroleum,* **40,** 140–5 (1963).
105. A. Cameron. *The principles of lubrication.* Longmans, 1966.
106. H. L. Mason. "Sensitivity and life data on Bourdon tubes". *Trans. ASME,* **78,** 65–77 (1956).
107. D. H. Newhall and L. H. Abbott. "The bulk modulus cell—new high pressure measuring instrument". *Chem. Eng. Progress,* **56,** 112–13 (1960).
108. D. H. Newhall and L. H. Abbott. "High pressure measurement". *Instruments and Control Systems,* **34,** 232–3 (1961).
109. E. Lisell. "On the effect of pressure on the electrical resistance of metals and the new methods of technique for measuring high pressures". *Upsala University Arsskrift,* No. 1 (1903).
110. P. W. Bridgman. "The measurement of hydrostatic pressures up to 20,000 kilograms per square centimeter". *Proc. Amer. Acad. Arts Sci.,* **47,** 321–43 (1911).
111. A. Michels and M. Lenssen. "An electric manometer for pressures up to 3000 atmospheres". *J. Sci. Inst.,* **11,** 345–7 (1934).
112. S. E. Babb. "Some notes concerning Bridgman's manganin pressure scale". In *High Pressure Measurement,* Butterworths, 1963.
113. Amagat, as quoted in Bridgman, Ref. 88.
114. P. W. Bridgman. "The linear compression of iron to 30,000 kg/cm^2". *Proc. Amer. Acad. Sci.,* **74,** 11–20 (1940).
115. E. F. Chandler. "Tensile properties of a number of materials under hydrostatic pressure". NEL Report No. 306, August 1967.
116. H. Ll. D. Pugh. "An intermittent (semi-continuous) hydrostatic extrusion machine". NEL Report No. 344, February 1968.
117. Anon. "1600/80 ton hydrostatic extrusion press". *The Engineer,* 8 September 1967, 312–14.

118. F. J. Fuchs, Jr. "Production metal forming with hydrostatic pressures". ASME Paper No. 65-PROD-17, 1965.
119. S. Johnsson. "Fortschritte beim Hydrostatischen Strangpressen". *Bender Bleche Rohre*, **9** (6) (June 1968).
120. S. Johnsson. "Recent developments of hydrostatic extrusion". *Wire World International*, **11** (1), 23–7 (1969).
121. R. J. Fiorentino, B. D. Richardson, A. M. Sabroff, and F. W. Boulger. "New developments in hydrostatic extrusion". Paper No. 3A5-3. International Conference on Manufacturing Technology, 1967. Published by the American Society of Tool and Manufacturing Engineers.
122. H. Ll. D. Pugh. "Hydrostatic extrusion". Paper No. 18. Ninth Commonwealth Mining and Metallurgical Congress (1969).
123. A. G. Rozner and J. E. Tydings. "Effect of hydrostatic extrusion on the mechanical properties of CuZn and TiNi". *J. Instn Met.*, **95,** 254–5 (1967).
124. Th. von Kármán. "Strength investigations under hydrostatic pressure". *Zeitschrift V.D.I.* **55,** 1749 (1911).
125. P. W. Bridgman. "The effect of pressure on the tensile properties of several metals and other materials". *J. Appl. Phys.*, **24,** 560 (1953).
126. B. Crossland. "The effect of fluid pressure on the shear properties of metals". *Proc. Instn Mech. Engrs*, **168,** 935 (1954).
127. T. Pelczynski. "The influence of hydrostatic pressure on the plastic properties of metals". *Archiwum Hutnictaw*, **7,** (1), 3–12 (1962).
128. H. Ll. D. Pugh and D. Green. "The effects of hydrostatic pressure on the plastic flow and fracture of metals". *Proc. Instn Mech. Engrs*, **179** (1) (1964–5).
129. E. D. Martynov, B. I. Beresnev, D. K. Bulychev, K. P. Rodionov and Yu. N. Ryabinin. "Influence of high pressure on the ductility and fracture of metals". *VSB. Mek. Plast-deformtsii Met. Kiev, Nauk*, Dumka-4-28 (1965).
130. B. Crossland and W. H. Dearden. "The plastic flow and fracture of a 'brittle' material (grey cast iron) with particular reference to the effect of fluid pressure". *Proc. Instn Mech. Engrs*, **172** (26), 805–20 (1958).
131. H. Ll. D. Pugh and D. Gunn. "The cold extrusion of brittle materials against a liquid pressure". Symposium on the Physics and Chemistry of High Pressures. Society of Chemical Industry, 1963.
132. G. S. Lawson. "Mechanical properties of cold extruded aluminium rods". NEL Report No. 51, September 1962.

133. W. S. Farren and G. I. Taylor. "The heat developed during plastic extension of metals". *Proc. Roy. Soc.*, A, **107,** 422–51 (1924–5).
134. F. J. Fuchs. "High pressure continuous wire extrusion". Research report, Western Electric Co., Princeton, N.J., U.S.A.
135. D. Green, "Hydrospin, a new concept of extrusion", *J. Inst. Metals*, **99,** 76–80 (1971).
136. R. J. Fiorentino, B. D. Richardson and A. M. Sabroff. "Hydrostatic extrusion of brittle materials. Role of die design and residual stress formation". *Metal Forming*, September 1969, 243–52.
137. S. Thiruvarudchelvan and J. M. Alexander. "Hydrodynamic lubrication in hydrostatic extrusion using a double reduction die". 11th M.T.D.R. Conf., September 1970, University of Birmingham.
138. J. M. Alexander and S. Kamyab. "Determination of die stresses and temperatures in hydrostatic extrusion". Imperial College, unpublished.

SUBJECT INDEX

AUTHOR INDEX

LIST OF SYMBOLS IN CHAPTER 3

A_1	initial cross sectional area of the billet
A_2	final cross sectional area of the product
$a\ b\ a'\ b'$	constants
E	Young's modulus
E_t	tangent modulus
$f(\alpha)$	determined by equation 5, represents redundant work in the conical portion of the die
H	thickness of fluid layer at the billet/die interface
I	second moment of area of the billet cross section
k	shear yield stress of the billet material
L	axial length of the die-land
l	length of billet
m	constant
N	"modified" Sommerfeld number
p	extrusion pressure
P_{CR}	buckling load
q_b	fluid pressure surrounding the billet
q_f	fluid pressure surrounding the product
R	Extrusion ratio $\left(=\frac{A_1}{A_2}\right)$
R_i	initial billet radius
R_f	final product radius
r	fractional reduction of billet $\left[=1-\left(\frac{R_f}{R_i}\right)^2\right]$
$R_{max(s)}$	limiting extrusion ratio when s_{max} is applied
$R_{o\ max(s)}$	limiting extrusion ratio related to the original billet diameter when s_{max} is applied
R_{max}	limiting extrusion ratio for orthodox hydrostatic extrusion
$R_{max(t)}$	limiting extrusion ratio when t_{max} is applied
s	compressive stress superimposed on the billet
s_{CR}	critical buckling stress
s_{max}	maximum compressive stress which can be applied to the billet
t	tensile stress superimposed on the product
t_{max}	maximum tensile stress which can be applied to the product

v	velocity of billet material over the die face
v_i	initial billet velocity
v_f	final product velocity
Υ	uniaxial yield stress of the billet material
Υ_m	mean yield stress of the billet material
α	die semi-angle
ε	strain
$\bar{\varepsilon}$	equivalent strain
ε_1	redundant strain in crossing the entry and exit boundaries
ε_2	total strain before crossing the exit boundary
ε_3	final total strain
Γ_1	spherical surface of velocity discontinuity at the die exit
Γ_2	spherical surface of velocity discontinuity at the die entry
Γ_3	conical billet/die interface
Γ_4	cylindrical product/die interface
μ	Coulomb coefficient of friction
$\bar{\sigma}$	equivalent stress
σ_0	constant flow stress
σ_{xb}	pressure acting on the billet in the high pressure chamber ($= q_b + s$)
σ_{xf}	pressure acting on the product in the low pressure chamber ($= q_f - t$)
τ	surface shear stress due to viscous shearing of the lubricant

LIST OF SYMBOLS IN CHAPTER 4

A	cross sectional area of the billet at any given position within the die
A_2	cross sectional area of the billet at die exit
c	radius of the plastic-elastic interface
$e\theta_2$	hoop strain on the outside of the cylinder
e_z	axial strain
E	Young's modulus
K	diameter ratio $\left(= \dfrac{\text{outside diameter}}{\text{inside diameter}} \text{ of the cylinder}\right)$
$K_1\, K_2 \ldots K_n$	diameter ratio of the first, second, n^{th} component cylinder of the compound container

M & B MONOGRAPHS

MECHANICAL ENGINEERING

ME/1 Tribology 0.263.51588.5
E D Hondros

ME/2 Electron Beam Welding 0.263.51707.1
M J Fletcher

ME/3 Vacuum Brazing 0.263.51708.x
M J Fletcher

ME/4 Stress Corrosion Failure 0.263.51725.x
P Greenfield

ME/5 Glow Discharge Material Processing 0.263.51787.x
R A Dugdale

ME/6 Diamond Grinding 0.263.51791.8
J Burls

CHEMICAL ENGINEERING

CE/1 Microbiological Corrosion 0.263.515842
G H Booth

CE/2 Solvent Treatment of Coal 0.263.51706.3
W S Wise

CE/3 The Fluidised Combustion of Coal 0.263.51714.4
D G Skinner

CE/4 Carbonisation of Coal 0.263.51774.8
J Gibson D H Gregory

CE/5 The Principles of Gas Extraction 0.263.51802.7
P Paul W S Wise

CE/6 Metal-Air Batteries 0.263.51838.8
D P Gregory

ELECTRICAL ENGINEERING

EE/1 Threshold Logic 0.263.51587.7
S L Hurst

EE/2 The Magnetron Oscillator 0.263.51641.5
E Kettlewell

EE/3 Material for the Gunn Effect 0.263.51773.x
J W Orton

EE/4 Microcircuit Learning Computers 0.263.51724.1
I Aleksander

EE/5 D C Conduction in Thin Films 0.263.51786.1
J G Simmons

EE/6 Reading Machines 0.263.51839.6
J A Weaver

M & B TECHNICAL LIBRARY

TL/ME/1	**Hydrostatic Extrusion** J M Alexander B Lengyel	0.263.51709.8
TL/ME/2	**The Heat Pipe** D Chisholm	0.263.51711.x
TL/CE/1	**Boron** A G Massey J Kane	0.263.51775.6
TL/EE/1	**Linear Electric Motors** E R Laithwaite	0.263.51586.9
TL/EE/2	**An Introduction to the Josephson Effects** B W Petley	0.263.51705.5

FORTHCOMING TITLES

Engineering Applications of Beryllium
P Greenfield
Whiskers C C Evans
Creep of Metals P Greenfield
Cavitation I S Pearsall

Fuel Cells D P Gregory

Speech Synthesis J N Holmes
Glow Discharge Display G F Weston

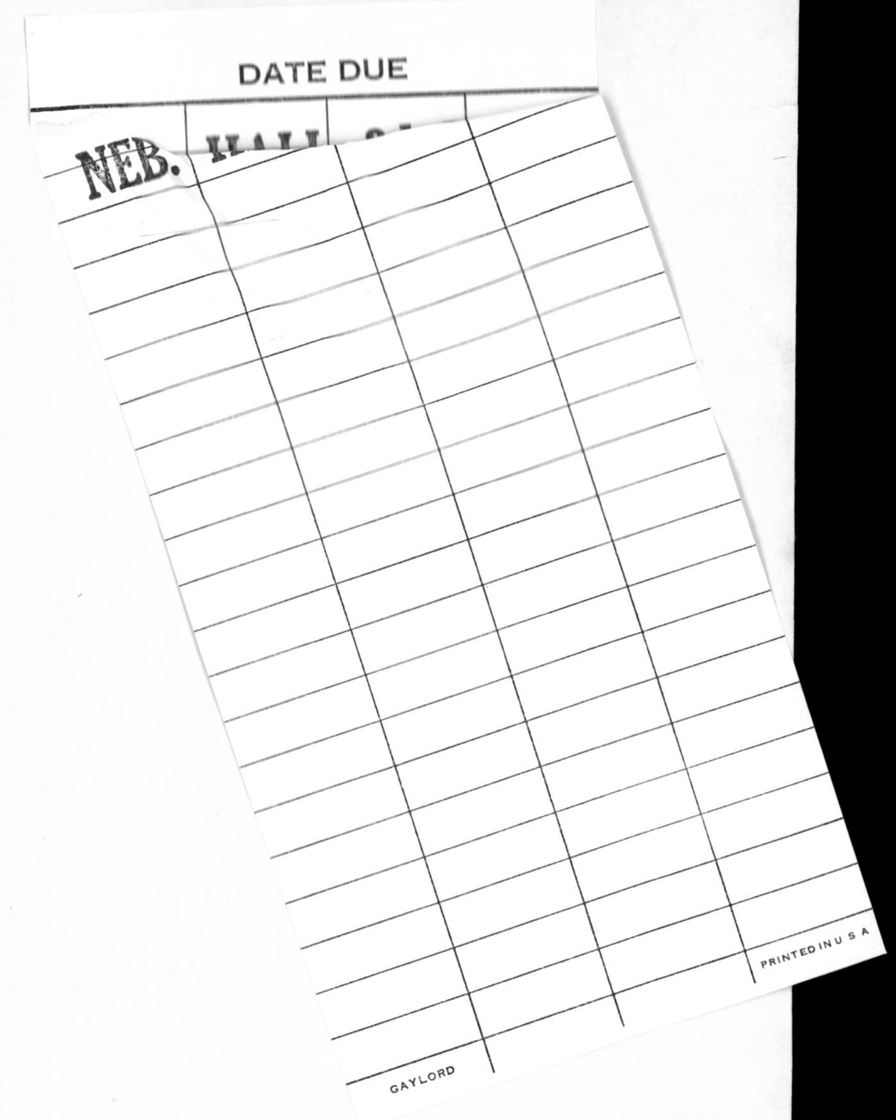
DATE DUE
NEB.
GAYLORD
PRINTED IN U.S.A.